G000139224

Cell motility

Integrated Themes in Biology

Consulting editor: *I. D. J. Phillips, University of Exeter*

Hall and Baker: Cell membranes and ion transport
Milburn: Water flow in plants
Pitt: Lysosomes and cell function
Stebbings and Hyams: Cell motility
Whittaker and Danks: Mitochondria

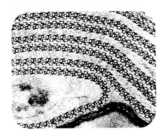

Cell motility

Howard Stebbings

Department of Biological Sciences
University of Exeter

Jeremy S. Hyams

Department of Botany and Microbiology
University College London

Longman London and New York

Longman Group Limited London

Associated companies, branches and representatives
throughout the world

Published in the United States of America
by Longman Inc., New York

© Longman Group Limited 1979

All rights reserved. No part of this publication may be
reproduced, stored in a retrieval system, or transmitted
in any form or by any means, electronic, mechanical,
photocopying, recording, or otherwise, without the
prior permission of the Copyright owner.

First published 1979

British Library Cataloguing in Publication Data

Stebbings, Howard
  Cell motility. – (Integrated themes in biology).
  1. Cells – Motility
  I. Title   II. Hyams, Jeremy S   III. Series
  574.8'764   QH647   78–40543

  ISBN 0–582–44380–6

Printed in Great Britain by
Whitstable Litho Ltd., Whitstable, Kent

Contents

Preface

Since the introduction of the earliest microscopes, biologists have been fascinated by the movement of cells. The frenetic swimming motions of spermatozoa, the streaming of plant cell protoplasm and the peripatetic gliding movements of amoebae were all extensively documented long before the turn of the century. Despite the limitations imposed by the resolution of their instruments, many of the observations have proved extremely accurate and moreover were interpreted with considerable insight, so much so, that they have often provided the basis for subsequent studies.

With the advent of the electron microscope a new dimension to the study of cell motility was introduced. Now it became possible, for the first time, to look inside the cell and to identify structures associated with cell movements. Initially progress was steady rather than spectacular; many problems relating to fixation and specimen preservation had to be overcome. However, a picture gradually emerged in which two classes of minute fibrous structures, referred to as *microtubules* and *microfilaments,* were almost invariably found in the region of the cell in which movement occurred. Concurrently with this increase of information regarding cell ultrastructure, a rapid improvement in the technology of cell fractionation and purification laid cell motility open to the biochemists, and our understanding of its molecular basis rapidly advanced.

It is now clear that there are many more compelling reasons to study cell movement than the natural beauty and fascination which attracted the first microscopists. Such problems as sperm function and fertility, the development and function of the nervous system and the invasive nature of cancer cells are three of the central questions of biological and medical sciences which fall within its compass. For this reason cell motility has in recent years seen an enormous accumulation of interest, to the extent that it is without doubt one of the most productive areas of modern cell biology.

Our intention in producing this text is to provide students with an introduction to many of the problems which concern workers in the area of cell motility, to describe some of the systems currently being investigated, and to discuss the various concepts regarding motile mechanisms which have so far emerged.

We are indebted to all the authors who have generously supplied illustrations which are so essential for a text of this nature.

H. Stebbings and J. S. Hyams
Exeter, Devon. 1978

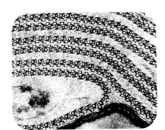

Chapter 1

Structure, biochemistry and function of striated muscle

At first glance it may seem incongruous to begin a volume devoted to the movement of non-muscle cells in its many guises with a consideration of the mechanism of muscle contraction. Virtually all the examples of cell motility which we shall consider in this book, however, share one common feature, namely they require the conversion of chemical energy, synthesised by metabolic activity and stored primarily in the form of adenosine triphosphate (ATP), into mechanical work. In striated muscle this transduction of chemical energy into force production has evolved to a staggering efficiency. The flight muscles of insects, for example, are capable of producing a power output comparable to that of certain internal combustion engines and can exert a tension equivalent to several kilograms for each square centimetre of their cross-sectional area. Increasingly, however, the organisation and function of striated muscle have come to be regarded as highly specialised manifestations of a property which is fundamental to many other less specialised cells. Hence, although the force generation required to propel an amoeba on its gliding meanderings across its substrate, or to constrict an animal cell at cytokinesis, is infinitesimal when compared to the violent contraction of muscle fibres, the proteins involved and the mechanisms by which they interact may be analogous. The arguments for and against this view are considered in some detail in subsequent chapters. What is without doubt is that our current understanding of cell motility in its many and diverse forms has been profoundly influenced and perhaps even biased by the classical and elegant studies of muscle contraction.

In the following sections, we make no attempt to provide a

1

comprehensive review of muscle physiology but rather to introduce concepts and principles which, as will become increasingly apparent in later chapters, are vital to a clear understanding of the motility of non-muscle cells.

1.1 Structure of vertebrate striated muscle

Vertebrate striated muscle has been much more extensively studied than other muscle types, largely because the regularity of its structure makes it particularly suitable for ultrastructural investigation, but also, since it comprises the large lifting and running muscles of vertebrates, it is available in large quantities for biochemical studies. Striated skeletal muscle consists of three distinct components:

1. Multinucleate cylindrical myofibres which are the contractile machinery of the muscle. (These range from 10–100 μm in diameter and extend up to several centimetres in length.)
2. Mitochondria which produce ATP, the fuel for contraction.
3. The sarcotubular system which is a system of membrane-bound channels thought to coordinate the contraction of the fibres.
See Fig. 1.1.

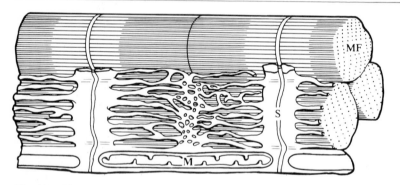

Fig. 1.1 Diagram illustrating the essential elements of striated skeletal muscle. The diagram shows the arrangement of the banded myofibrils (MF), mitochondria (M) and sarcotubular system (S).

Myofibres in turn are composed of a system of elongated elements 1–2 μm in diameter and called *myofibrils*. These are the basic contractile units of the muscle fibre and the term 'striated' derives from the in register periodic repeats which they exhibit along their length. Examination of striated muscle by light microscopy reveals that each myofibril is subdivided into repeating units known as *sarcomeres*, which are separated by regularly spaced dense Z lines (from German *zwichen* = between). The myofibrils also show a regular pattern of banding which is seen particularly clearly using polarising microscopy. At either end of a sarcomere is a less dense region forming the I band (as it appears isotropic) and between these is the A band (anisotropic) which has greater density except for a central H zone (from German *hell* = clear).

Electron microscopy has shown that the basis of the banding lies in a highly ordered arrangement of myofilaments within each sarcomere (Fig. 1.2). The filaments are of two kinds – thick (10–12 nm in

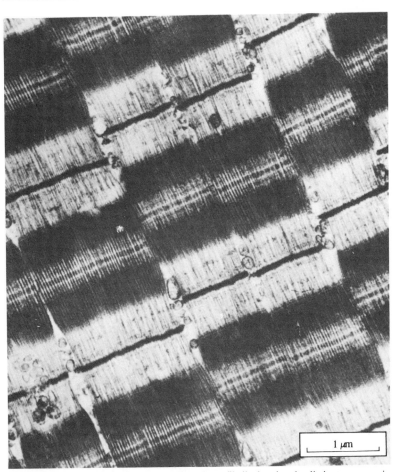

Fig. 1.2 Longitudinal section of a number of myofibrils showing the distinct sarcomeric structure. (Courtesy of Dr H. E. Huxley.)

diameter) and thin (5–8 nm), the banding resulting from the degree of overlap of the in register filaments (Fig. 1.3).

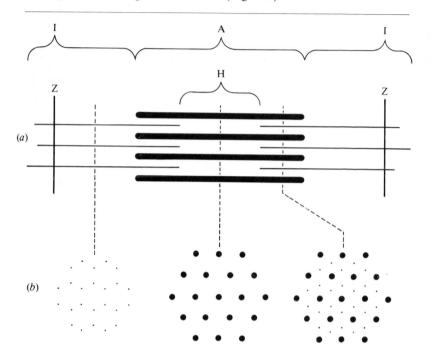

Fig. 1.3 Diagram showing the arrangement of thin and thick filaments within a single sarcomere of striated muscle. The overlapping of filaments gives rise to the characteristic banding pattern and can be seen in either longitudinal (*a*) or transverse (*b*) section.

Hence, as we can see from the figure, the I bands contain only thin filaments, and the H bands only thick filaments, while the A bands are regions where thick and thin filaments overlap. The geometric arrangement of the two types of filament with respect to each other can be discerned most clearly from transverse sections (Figs. 1.3 and 1.4). These show that each thick filament is surrounded by an hexagonal array of thin filaments and that each thin filament is therefore bounded by three thick ones. Furthermore, in both transverse and longitudinal sections (Fig. 1.5), bridges can be seen extending from the thick filaments towards the thin filaments.

Upon contraction, the organisation of the sarcomere as seen in the light microscope undergoes pronounced changes. While the A band remains constant the I band is reduced proportionately to the degree of shortening. As we shall see in more detail later, these observations

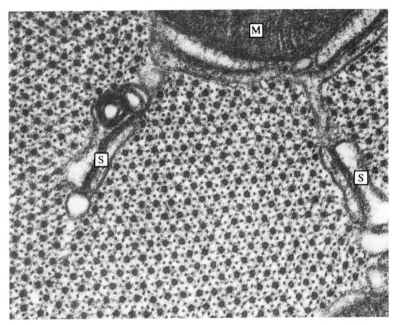

Fig. 1.4 Transverse section of a myofibril showing the hexagonal packing of thin and thick filaments. (M) mitochondrion; (S) sarcotubular system.

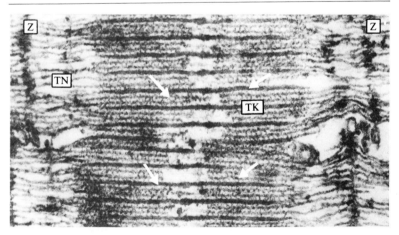

Fig. 1.5 High magnification of a single sarcomere. Bridges can be clearly seen extending between the thick (TK) and the thin (TN) filaments (arrows). (Courtesy of Dr H. E. Huxley.)

have been interpreted as reflecting alterations in the degree of overlap between the two classes of filament as they move or slide across each other while undergoing no change in length themselves. If correct, this mechanism implies that contraction of the muscle fibre can be understood in terms of the molecules which comprise the structural elements of the sarcomere. It is therefore pertinent to ask several questions: what are the thick and thin filaments composed of? what is the nature of the bridges extending between them? how do the two types of filament interact? and how is the interaction controlled?

1.2 Biochemistry of muscle proteins

The complex, three-dimensional architecture of the sarcomere revealed by the electron microscope is composed almost entirely of four proteins, *actin*, *myosin*, *tropomyosin* and *troponin*. Of these, actin and myosin account for some 80% of the total and on this basis alone are likely to be of primary importance to the process of muscle contraction.

Actin and myosin are sequentially extracted when muscle fibres are exposed to fairly concentrated salt solutions, usually between 0.3–0.6 M KCl. Myosin is solubilised very rapidly by this method while the extraction of actin is achieved only by more prolonged treatment. The removal of the two proteins is accompanied by characteristic changes in the pattern of striations of the sarcomere seen in the light microscope. Separation of myosin results in the disappearance of the A band while the displacement of actin is contiguous with a marked reduction in the intensity of the I band. These observations provided the first indication that actin and myosin could be equated with the thin and thick filaments of the myofibril respectively, a conclusion which subsequently has been emphatically confirmed by a variety of analytical procedures.

Although as we shall see later, actin and myosin differ widely in their physical properties, the two proteins interact very strongly, a fact first recognised in a series of pioneering experiments in the early 1940s (Szent-Györgyi, 1951). During this period it was discovered that solutions of actin and myosin, mixed together in the presence of high salt, rapidly became extremely viscous due to the formation of an *actomyosin* complex. Upon the addition of ATP (adenosine triphosphate), the fuel by which muscle contraction is powered, the viscosity of the mixture at first declined to its original level but then slowly began to rise again. ATP therefore appeared to reverse the physical association between actin and myosin while itself being consumed by the reaction. The obvious inference of such a finding is that the actomyosin mixture possessed *ATPase activity*, that is it contained an enzyme capable of cleaving the terminal phosphate group of ATP and hence liberating energy for mechanical work.

With increasing sophistication in the technology of preparing the muscle proteins it was clearly established that this enzymatic activity was an integral property of the myosin molecule. However, the rate at which myosin catalysed the hydrolysis of ATP in the presence of magnesium, the most abundant sarcoplasmic ion, was found to be extremely slow, some hundredfold less than other enzymes of this type and therefore far too inefficient to account for the rapid consumption of ATP during muscle activity. At least a partial resolution of this dilemma was provided by the key discovery that in the presence of actin, myosin ATPase was dramatically stimulated, sufficient to now suggest that the hydrolysis of ATP by myosin, *in association with actin*, is the force-generating reaction of contraction.

Further evidence for this possibility was obtained experimentally by Szent-Györgyi in a very direct way. By extruding actomyosin solutions from a fine capillary into dilute salt solutions he formed slender, filamentous precipitates which he called 'threads'. Incredibly, upon the addition of ATP, these actomyosin threads were seen to contract, or in other words, mixtures of purified actin and myosin were capable of generating movements reminiscent of the muscle fibre from which they were derived.

That the properties of the actomyosin threads corresponded in some meaningful way to the situation in the muscle fibre was clearly suggested by the behaviour of glycerinated myofibrils. Exposure of isolated myofibrils for several days at 0°C to an aqueous 50% glycerol solution resulted in the extraction of the surrounding membrane and all soluble proteins, leaving behind essentially a cytoskeletal framework of actin and myosin molecules. As with the actomyosin threads, these glycerinated 'models' also contracted upon the addition of ATP. Both of these artificial preparations, however, differed from living muscle in one important aspect, namely, that once contracted they were not capable of subsequent relaxation. Both therefore can be regarded as being in *rigor*, a condition associated with muscle in death (hence rigor mortis) where the loss of ATP causes the fibres to become rigid and inextensible.

Relaxation was shown by Ebashi in the 1960s to depend upon the introduction of yet another factor, extracted from muscle by treatment with dilute salt solutions. This fraction, which had first been isolated twenty years previously and designated 'native tropomyosin', allowed the contracted system to relax but only if the level of calcium in the reaction solution was lowered to below 10^{-8} M. At the same time the presence of native tropomyosin inhibited the syneresis, and hence the ATPase activity, of actomyosin unless the calcium ion concentration was once again raised above 10^{-5} M. In the jargon of the biochemist, native tropomyosin is therefore said to confer *calcium sensitivity* to the actin–myosin–ATP interaction. Hence contraction proceeds at elevated levels of calcium while relaxation requires the level of calcium ions to be lowered, the transition being under the direct influence of native tropomyosin. Subsequently it has been shown that native tropomyosin is in fact a complex of two proteins, tropomyosin and troponin, and the role of these molecules in the regulation of muscle contraction *in vivo* has been amply confirmed.

1.2.1 Thick filament

The thick filament of the myofibril is composed exclusively of a single protein, myosin, which comprises some 50% of the total structural protein of striated muscle. Myosin is a complicated molecule, sufficiently large to be visualised in the electron microscope where it is seen to consist of a long rod-like tail and a bilobed globular head (Fig. 1.6). The size of the molecule is reflected in its enormous molecular weight of 470,000 daltons. This is composed of two heavy chains each of approximately 200,000 daltons plus four light chains, each around 20,000 daltons, although the precise details may vary among different types of muscle. The heavy chains constitute the helical tail of the molecule together with most of the globular head region while the light chains are confined exclusively to the head.

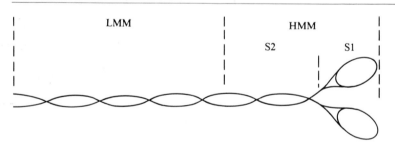

Fig. 1.6 Diagram of a myosin molecule showing the position of enzymatic cleavage into light meromyosin (LMM) and heavy meromyosin (HMM) and the subfragments of HMM, S1 and S2.

Treatment of myosin with the proteolytic enzyme trypsin, digests the molecule into two fragments. *Heavy meromyosin* or HMM consists of the two globular heads plus about a third of the tail portion and contains all the ATPase activity of the protein. *Light meromyosin* or LMM is an α helical, rod-shaped molecule consisting of the rest of the myosin tail. HMM may be further cleaved either by extended trypsin treatment or by another protease, papain, into two smaller fragments designated S1 and S2 (for subfragment 1 and 2; Fig. 1.6). S1 consists of just the head of the myosin molecule while S2 is the small portion of the tail associated with HMM. Enzymatic activity has been found to be associated only with S1 and this has led to the hypothesis that in the thick filament the myosin molecules are organised in such a way that this portion of the molecule projects towards the thin filament with which it undergoes cycles of attachment and detachment, causing the two filaments to slide over one another (Section 1.3). S2 has different chemical properties from the rest of the myosin tail (LMM) and probably is also important in this cross-bridge reaction, possibly acting as a swivel upon which the S1 component pivots.

The possible involvement of S1 in a reversible interaction with the thin filament has been emphatically and elegantly demonstrated by Huxley who showed that either HMM or S1 would interact with purified actin filaments *in vitro* to form a highly specific and characteristic *arrowhead* complex which is clearly revealed by negative staining (Fig. 1.7) and results from the attachment of the myosin

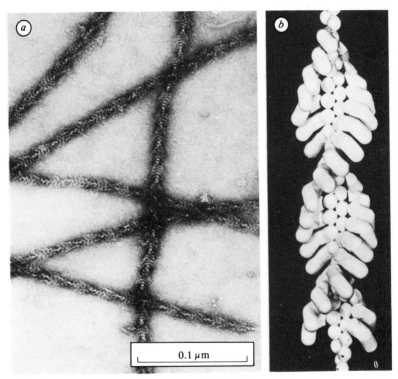

0.1 μm

Fig. 1.7 Decoration of actin filaments with HMM. (*a*) negatively stained preparation showing the arrowhead complexes and (*b*) a three-dimensional model showing the attachment of the HMM to the actin helix. ((a) Courtesy of Dr H. E. Huxley; (b) from H. E. Huxley, *Proc. Roy. Inst. Gr. Br.*, **44**, 274 (1970).)

fragment at a periodicity of 36 nm. More importantly, in the presence of ATP, which causes the detachment of cross-bridges during muscular contraction, the binding of the arrowheads was reversed. So specific is the arrowhead decoration of actin filaments by HMM or S1 that this technique has become widely used as a cytological probe for the identification of actin filaments (microfilaments) in a wide variety of non-muscle cells.

Under physiological conditions, myosin molecules will spontaneously assemble into bipolar aggregates resembling the thick filaments of the myofibril (Fig. 1.8). These consist of a bare central shaft, 150 nm long by 2–3 nm in diameter, with projections containing the ATPase activity and actin binding sites at each end.

Fig. 1.8 Diagram showing the bipolar arrangement of myosin molecules within the thick filament. The tails of the myosin molecules make up the backbone of the filament with the heads projecting from either end.

From X-ray and electron microscope data a picture of these synthetic filaments has emerged which supposes the tails of the myosin molecules overlap with their heads projecting from opposite ends. Further evidence that this interpretation may in fact be the correct one comes from synthetic filaments similarly assembled from LMM alone. Such structures are, as expected, completely smooth and lack the lateral projections of the myosin heads.

1.2.2 Thin filament

The thin filament of vertebrate striated muscle is composed of the three remaining major structural proteins of the sarcomere, namely, actin, tropomyosin and troponin in the ratio of 7:1:1. Actin which comprises 25–30% of the total muscle protein forms the backbone of the thin filament upon which the two others are organised.

Actin   In solution, actin appears as a spherical, globular subunit approximately 5.5 nm in diameter. The protein is composed of a single polypeptide chain of 376 amino acids whose sequence has been completely determined (Elzinga and Collins, 1973) and from which a molecular weight of 42,000 daltons has been calculated. Perhaps the most interesting feature to emerge from analysis of the amino acid composition is the presence at position 73 of a single residue of the rare amino acid N^τ-methylhistidine. Although the significance of this observation is not immediately obvious, the presence of this unusual amino acid has become a useful diagnostic tool for the identification of actin in non-muscle cells.

Upon raising the salt concentration of actin solutions to 0.1 M KCl, *globular* or *G-actin* spontaneously polymerises into a double helical polymer referred to as *filamentous* or *F-actin* which closely resembles the thin filament of the myofibril (Fig. 1.9). F-actin consists of two strands of subunits resembling twin strands of pearls twisted around one another in a right-handed, two-start helix containing about 13 G-actin monomers every repeat unit, or crossover point, of 36 nm.

Each molecule of G-actin is associated with one molecule of bound adenine nucleotide, usually in the form of ATP. Polymerisation is accompanied by hydrolysis of the terminal phosphate of the bound

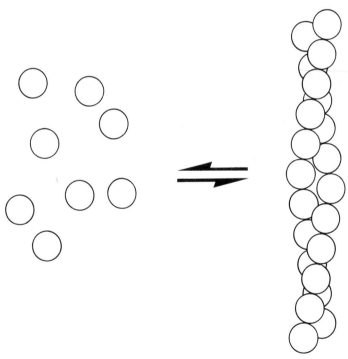

Fig. 1.9 Diagram showing the equilibrium between actin subunits and the assembled double helical polymer.

ATP according to the following scheme:

$$n \text{ (G-actin.ATP)} \rightleftharpoons \text{F-actin.ADP} + n\text{Pi}$$

Recent evidence strongly indicates that energy liberated by the hydrolysis is not, as was originally supposed, used to drive the polymerisation reaction. Experimentally modified G-actin with no bound nucleotide or with either ADP (adenosine diphosphate) or AMPPNP (adenylyl imidodiphosphate, a non-hydrolysable ATP analogue) in the place of ATP will still assemble into filaments under the appropriate conditions (Cooke, 1975). One possible function of the bound nucleotide, however, may be to preserve the native configuration of the subunit. This is suggested by the finding that the capacity of G-actin, with bound ADP or AMPPNP, to assemble into filaments declined sharply over extended periods of time while native G-actin.ATP remained competent to undergo the G–F transformation. Whatever the role of bound nucleotide is finally discovered to be, its presence, like that of the amino acid N^{τ}-methylhistidine, is a characteristic which has greatly aided the identification of actin in other cells.

Tropomyosin   Tropomyosin is a protein with a molecular weight of 70,000 daltons which, together with troponin, constitutes about 15% of the total muscle protein. The molecule is composed of two subunits designated α and β which are identical, or nearly so, depending on the source. Each is a helical chain, the two being wound around one another to form a coiled coil. Tropomyosin may be crystallised *in vitro*, a property which has greatly facilitated the investigation of the structure of the molecule by electron microscopy and X-ray diffraction. These techniques have shown that tropomyosin is a rod-shaped molecule, 40 nm in length by about 2–3 nm in diameter. By the use of fluorescein or ferritin-labelled tropomyosin antibodies it has

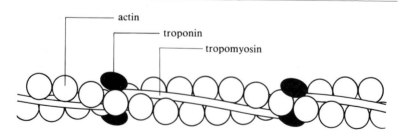

Fig. 1.10   Diagram of the thin myofilament showing the three components actin, troponin and tropomyosin.

also been possible to demonstrate that the protein is distributed along the whole length of the thin filament of the myofibril where it is located in the groove between the two actin chains, each molecule covering seven actin subunits of one strand (Fig. 1.10). Considerable evidence now indicates that slight shifts in the position of the tropomyosin molecule under the influence of troponin can either mask or uncover sites of interaction between actin and myosin and hence regulate their interaction.

Troponin   Troponin is a globular protein with a molecular weight of 76,000 daltons which attaches to a single molecule of tropomyosin about one-third of the way along its length (Fig. 1.10). The protein is composed of three subunits, each of which has a specific and distinct function from which its nomenclature is derived as follows: TnT (tropomyosin-binding subunit), TnI (ATPase-inhibiting subunit) and TnC (calcium-binding subunit).

Subunit TnC has a molecular weight of 18,000 daltons and undergoes a marked conformational change in the presence of calcium which alters its interactions with the other subunits. TnI (21,000 daltons) strongly inhibits the ATPase activity of actomyosin while at the same time increasing the affinity of tropomyosin for actin. This latter reaction is probably responsible for locating tropomyosin in its correct position on the actin molecule. TnT binds strongly to tropomyosin and is thought to be responsible for attaching the troponin molecule to tropomyosin. The effect of this subunit can be clearly demonstrated *in vitro* where it causes very obvious changes in both the packing of tropomyosin crystals and the sedimentation of tropomyosin in the ultracentrifuge. In the presence of TnC however, these altered states of tropomyosin induced by TnT are no longer observed.

We can summarise this information regarding the troponin subunits and their function in regulating the interaction between actin and myosin in the following way. The binding of calcium to TnC results in a stronger interaction between the three troponin subunits and a reduction in the affinity of TnI for tropomyosin. This latter reaction permits a slight movement of the tropomyosin molecule in the groove of the actin helix thus exposing sites on the actin molecule which interact with myosin. It is important to note that this situation does not apply to the muscles of certain invertebrates where regulation by calcium is not achieved via a troponin–tropomyosin complex (although these proteins may be present) but rather at the level of the myosin molecule itself. This situation is referred to as thick filament control to contrast it with the situation described above (thin filament control) which is typical of all vertebrates.

13

1.3 Sliding filament theory of muscle contraction

As can be seen from phase microscopy, when a muscle shortens the distance between the Z discs lessens and they are drawn towards the A band with a decrease in the size of the I band. Indeed, while the width of the A bands remains unchanged during contraction, the I and the H bands become progressively narrower and may even disappear altogether. Such changes in banding were first correlated with changes in the positioning of the myofilaments within the sarcomeres by Huxley and Hanson (1954) and Huxley and Niedergerke (1954). Both groups showed that the changes in appearance could be accounted for by the sliding of the thin and the thick filaments past each other without any change in the actual lengths of the filaments themselves (Fig. 1.11) and this has led to the now widely accepted *sliding filament theory* of muscle contraction.

The important question which then followed, was how the relative sliding of the two precisely arranged populations of filaments was

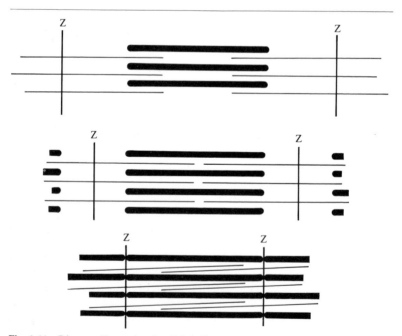

Fig. 1.11 Diagram illustrating the sliding filament model of muscle contraction. The degree of overlap of the thin and thick myofilaments increases during contraction, while the lengths of the filaments themselves remain constant.

brought about. What was clear, was that the force generated was proportional to the extent to which the thin and thick filaments overlapped, implying of course that the force was produced by an interaction between them. This focused attention on the relationship between the filaments and particularly the cross-bridges which are associated with them. The bridges themselves, as we have discussed, represent the head (S1) portion of the myosin molecules comprising the thick filaments, which contain the ATPase activity. A number of hypotheses have been proposed to explain how the S1 cross-bridges might interact with adjacent actin filaments to produce the sliding. Basically it has been envisaged that a cross-bridge binds to a specific site on the actin filament, whereupon it undergoes a conformational change using energy supplied by the splitting of ATP, thereby exerting a pull on the actin filament. One cycle would then be completed if a second cross-bridge became attached to the actin filament and the first returned to its original position. The model supposes of course that the myosin heads are attached flexibly to the myosin backbone (Fig. 1.12).

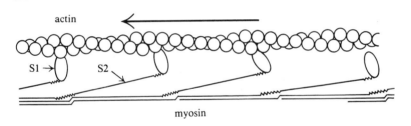

Fig. 1.12 Model depicting a sequence of attachment, tilting and detachment of myosin cross-bridges (S1 subunit) to an actin filament which results in a relative sliding between the two components. (After H. E. Huxley, (1976).)

In molecular terms the following sequence of events is thought to take place. First there is the formation of a linkage between the S1 head and one G-actin subunit. This is followed by the rupture of the link by one ATP molecule, and hydrolysis of the ATP by the ATPase of myosin. It will be appreciated that evidence in favour of this has been outlined in Section 1.2.1 where it was shown that either HMM or S1 attaches to actin filaments *in vitro* and is dissociated from them by ATP.

It is most important at this stage to appreciate the directionality of the actin and myosin filaments within a sarcomere. The primary prediction of the sliding filament theory is that the polarity in each half of a sarcomere must be opposed, since the thin filaments at either end slide over the thick filaments in opposite directions, that is, each Z line is pulled towards the middle. We have already discussed the bipolarity of the thick myosin filaments, but it is necessary that the actin filaments at either end of a sarcomere also possess opposing polarities. That this is indeed the case has been beautifully demonstrated by Huxley (1963) who was able to isolate the I band (the thin filaments attached to the Z disc) of the sarcomere. When incubated with HMM, arrowheads on either side of the Z disc, as predicted, pointing in opposite directions (Fig. 1.13).

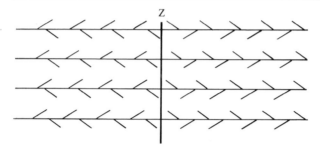

Fig. 1.13 Diagram illustrating the polarity of thin myofilaments relative to the Z line, as demonstrated by HMM decoration.

Bearing in mind the nature of such polarity, the postulated movements of the myosin heads, while attached to actin filaments, would pull the actin filaments towards the centre of the sarcomere.

Apart from electron microscopical evidence, low angle X-ray diffraction studies of living contracting muscle under working conditions also support the sliding filament mechanism. First, such studies have confirmed that the thin and thick filaments do not themselves change in length during contraction. Second, since the volume of a muscle remains constant during contraction, then the spacing between the component actin and myosin filaments must vary accordingly, and this has been shown to be the case by measuring the equatorial X-ray reflections. Also, some understanding of the association between the S1 myosin heads and the actin filaments can be gained by comparing the X-ray diagrams of resting muscle with those in rigor. In the diagram from resting muscle there is a well-developed system of layer lines with a 43 nm axial repeat and a strong third-order meridional repeat at 14 nm which derives from a regular helical arrangement of S1 heads on the thick filaments. These bridges occur at intervals at 14 nm with a helical repeat of 43 nm. On going into rigor, however, the elimination of certain of these features from the axial X-ray diagram suggests that the helical arrangement is lost. In fact, the 43 nm spacing disappears but the 14 nm spacing remains. Such findings show that the cross-bridges must alter their position and adopt a less regular arrangement in contracting muscle. While the main part of the myosin filament remains unchanged during contraction the attachment of the S1 heads to it are, as predicted, relatively flexible.

By contrast, there is clear evidence that the attachment of the S1 heads to the actin filaments is a much more rigid arrangement, as one can see when one looks at the highly ordered 'decoration' of actin filaments with the S1 heads – evidence interpreted by Huxley (1976) as suggesting that the site at which the force originates is indeed the interacting surface of the myosin head and the monomer on the actin filament.

1.4 Control of contractility

The ability of a muscle fibre to contract is advantageous only if its activity is regulated with respect to the requirements of the organism as a whole. In striated muscle, activity is determined by impulses transmitted by the central nervous system. In physiological terms, these are manifested by changes in the concentration of calcium ions in the sarcoplasm by up to a thousandfold.

The dependence of muscle activity on Ca^{2+} has been known for over 30 years, since the discovery that injection of these ions into muscles stimulated contraction. More recently correlation of the fluctuation of intramuscular Ca^{2+} with contraction has been demonstrated elegantly by Ashley and Ridgway (1970) using aequorin, a bioluminescent protein extracted from jellyfish. This compound produces a luminescence, the intensity of which is quantitatively related to the concentration of Ca^{2+}. In this way it was possible to demonstrate that muscle injected with aequorin glowed when excited, and furthermore that the emission faded before the muscle reached maximum tension.

The availability of free Ca^{2+} at the myofibrils is linked with an associated network of membranes, collectively known as the sarcotubular system. This consists of longitudinal and transverse components which are differentiated into repeating units corresponding to the sarcomeres. The longitudinal component, which is thought to derive from the endoplasmic reticulum and is known as the sarcoplasmic reticulum, is composed of regularly arranged channels running parallel to the fibrils with terminal cisternae ending at the level of the I bands. By contrast, the transverse system is composed of channels which open to the cell surface and are thought to derive from the sarcolemma with which they are continuous. The sarcoplasmic reticulum is closely associated with the transverse or T system and, although they are not continuous with each other, together they are involved in the regulation of muscle contraction. It is thought that electrical stimulation of the muscle fibre results in a depolarisation of the T system which in turn brings about the release of Ca^{2+} from the sarcoplasmic reticulum into the myofibrils, causing contraction. Conversely, after contraction, the Ca^{2+} ions are taken up again by the sarcoplasmic reticulum whose membranes contain an active Ca^{2+} pump. Its compartments also contain proteins, such as calsequestrin, which tightly bind the accumulated Ca^{2+}.

At the molecular level, as we have described in Section 1.2.2, the regulatory role of calcium operates via the troponin–tropomyosin complex associated with the thin filament. The basis of this regulation lies in the fact that the troponin molecule can exist in either of two conformational states depending upon its interaction with calcium ions. In the absence of Ca^{2+}, troponin stimulates a tight association between tropomyosin and actin. The effect of this interaction is to obscure the site at which the myosin cross-bridge interacts with the thin filament and hence contraction is prevented. In the presence of Ca^{2+}, changes in the troponin molecule reduce the affinity of tropomyosin for actin, exposing the myosin binding site on the actin helix, and contraction proceeds.

During subsequent chapters, we will see how the structure, the biochemistry and the functioning of striated muscle compares with that of other motile systems and why a clear understanding of these properties of muscle has become so essential to an appreciation of cell motility as a whole.

Suggestions for further reading and references

Further reading

BENDALL, J. R. (1974) *Muscles, Molecules and Movement.* Elsevier, N.Y.
MANNHERZ, H. G. and GOODY, R. S. (1976) Proteins of contractile systems, *Ann. Rev. Biochem.,* **45,** 427–65.
WILKIE, D. R. (1976) *Muscle,* 2nd edn. Institute of Biology's Studies in Biology No. 11. Arnold.

References

ASHLEY, C. C. and RIDGWAY, E. B. (1970) On the relationships between membrane potential, calcium transient, and tension in single barnacle muscle fibres, *J. Physiol,* **209,** 105–30.
COOKE, R. (1975) The bound nucleotide of actin, *J. Supramol. Struct.,* **3,** 146–53.
ELZINGA, M. and COLLINS, J. H. (1973) The amino acid sequence of rabbit skeletal muscle actin, *Cold Spring Harb. Symp. Quart. Biol.,* **37,** 1–7.
HUXLEY, A. F. and NIEDERGERKE, R. (1954) Interference microscopy of living muscle fibres, *Nature,* **173,** 971–3.
HUXLEY, H. E. (1963) Electron microscope studies on the structure of natural and

synthetic filaments from striated muscle, *J. Mol. Biol.*, **7**, 281–308.

HUXLEY, H. E. (1976) The relevance of studies on muscle to problems of cell motility, in *Cell Motility*, pp. 115–26, eds R. Goldman, T. Pollard and J. Rosenbaum. Cold Spring Harbor Laboratory.

HUXLEY, H. E. and HANSON, J. (1954) Changes in the cross-striations of muscle during contraction and stretch and their structural interpretation, *Nature*, **173**, 973–6.

SZENT-GYÖRGYI, A. (1951) *Chemistry of Muscular Contraction*, 2nd edn. Academic Press, N.Y.

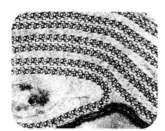

Chapter 2

Microtubules and microfilaments

It has become increasingly clear, with the development of electron microscopy and its associated preparative techniques, that two cytoplasmic fibrous elements, *microtubules* and *microfilaments*, while not reaching the high degree of organisation shown by muscle filaments, are specifically associated with a range of forms of cell motility. Microtubules were first named in 1963, when with the benefit of glutaraldehyde fixation small tubules were seen in the interstitial cells and cnidoblasts of *Hydra* (Slautterback, 1963) and also in plant cells (Ledbetter and Porter, 1963). Prior to this, they had only been observed as strands in shadowed preparations of dismembered cilia (Manton and Clarke, 1952) and in sectioned cilia as 11 filaments, drawn as circles in diagrams, arranged in a distinct 9 + 2 pattern (Fawcett and Porter, 1954). Besides cilia, fibrils with less dense centres had been seen in mitotic spindles, as well as in neurones and the cytoplasm of many protozoa. Since then, microtubules have been identified in almost all eukaryotic cells and, apart from ciliary, flagellar and spindle movements, are intimately involved in many other examples of cell motility.

Although research into microfilaments initially lagged behind that into microtubules, they too are found in both plant and animal cells, particularly those exhibiting cytoplasmic streaming and amoeboid movement, and their importance in a whole range of cell motile activities is becoming ever more apparent. Consequently, because almost all cellular motile systems appear to involve either microtubules or microfilaments or both, an entire chapter has been devoted to the biology of these two organelles.

20

2.1   Morphology of microtubules

Since the almost universal use of glutaraldehyde fixation, microtubules from a huge range of cells have consistently shown similar morphologies, though there are suggestions that this is dependent, to some extent, on the buffer used (Luftig *et al*., 1977) and whether the material is postfixed in osmium (Forer and Blecher, 1975). In transverse section microtubules appear as circles of between 20–24 nm diameter (although figures as large as 30 nm and as small as 18 nm have been reported) with an electron-dense wall approximately 5 nm thick around a less dense core of between 10–14 nm in width (Fig. 2.1*a*). In longitudinal section they are seen as two parallel electron-dense lines (Fig. 2.1*b*). Microtubules are long, apparently rigid structures, usually straight, but sometimes curved and occasionally they even follow a helical path.

While the disposition of microtubules within cells or cell processes can be determined from electron microscopical examination of thin sections, it has been discovered more recently that a better appreciation of their overall distribution may be obtained by means of immunofluorescence. In this technique, monospecific antibody is raised against purified microtubule protein in rabbits and used in one of two ways. For direct immunofluorescence, the antibody is conjugated with a fluorescent dye, such as fluorescein, and added directly to fixed, acetone-extracted cells. In the second method, indirect immunofluorescence, cells treated as previously are exposed to unconjugated antibody and then subsequently treated with fluorescent-labelled goat anti-rabbit serum. The distribution of the antibody in each case is seen in the light microscope by dark field, ultraviolet epi-illumination.

The immunofluorescence procedure has been shown to be particularly effective in the case of cultured cells from a wide variety of animals, since such cells are flattened and hence the microtubules tend to lie in a single focal plane (Weber *et al*., 1975). The technique reveals an extensive system of ramifying fibres, presumed to be microtubules, radiating from the region of the nucleus out to the cell periphery (Fig. 2.2*a*). The fact that no decorated fibres are seen after pretreatments which disrupt microtubules, and that the antiserum decorates well-known microtubule bundles, such as mitotic spindles, supports the view that microtubules can be visualised in this way. Indeed, although the dimensions of a microtubule are well below the limit of resolution of the light microscope, Weber and co-workers believe that individual microtubules can be resolved using the technique. Unfortunately it has not been possible to confirm this point by electron microscopy as the methodology of preparing cells for immunofluorescence results in poor preservation for ultrastructural

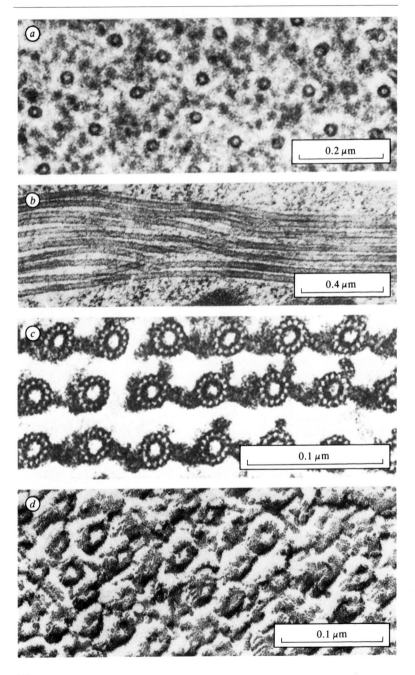

Fig. 2.1 Morphology of microtubules as seen in the electron microscope.
(*a*) Transverse section. Microtubules appear as dark circles with an apparently hollow centre. Each microtubule is surrounded by a clear zone into which the surrounding cytoplasmic constituents do not impinge. (*b*) Longitudinal section. Microtubules appear as narrow ribbons, usually straight but often, as here, following an undulatory path. (*c*) Transverse section, tannic acid fixation. Inclusion of tannic acid in the fixation solution permits the resolution of tubulin subunits which can be seen as 13 white dots around the microtubule wall. (*d*) Transverse section, freeze-etch replica. In the absence of any chemical fixatives the hollow nature of the microtubule and surrounding clear zone are still visible. ((*b*) From L. G. Tilney *et al.* (1973).)

studies. Despite this handicap, the method provides a simple and direct means of determining the distribution of microtubules and the changes which may occur in their organisation throughout the cell cycle.

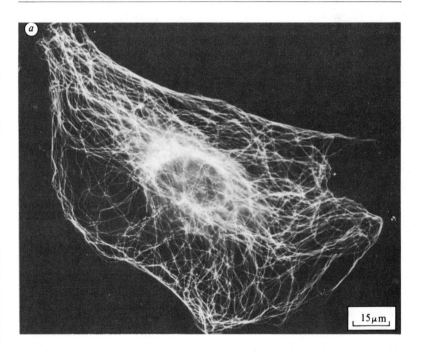

Fig. 2.2 Distribution of microtubules (*a*) and microfilaments (*b*) in mouse 3T3 cells as visualised by immunofluorescence. Microtubules appear as an intricate network of fine fibres radiating from the region of the nucleus. Microfilaments form bundles which lie parallel to the long axis of the cell. ((*a*) From K. Weber, in *Contractile Systems in Nonmuscle Tissue*, S. V. Perry, editor, (1976); (*b*) is from M. Osborn and K. Weber, *Exp. Cell Res.*, **106**, 339–49 (1977).)

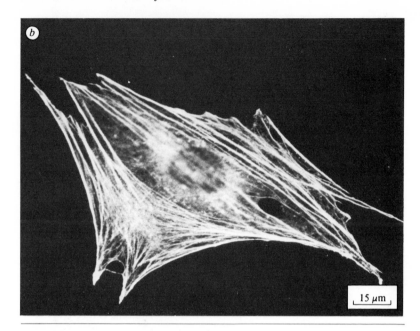

15 μm

2.1.1 Microtubule substructure

Something of the substructure of microtubules became clear when Ledbetter and Porter (1963) found, by chance, that microtubules in the meristematic cells of juniper stained in an unusual way, such that in transverse section their walls, which were as much as 7 nm thick, were seen to be composed of a number of subunits of circular outline. These subunits appeared negatively stained and had a centre to centre spacing of 4.5 nm. The photographic rotational reinforcement technique was used to determine the number of subunits in a single microtubule profile, and it was concluded that 13 was the most likely number in this instance. Although, in juniper, the subunits in the microtubule walls could be seen and counted, this situation was by no means usual and a great deal of speculation existed as to whether the number in other microtubules was the same. The question has now largely been answered, since the discovery that the negative staining effect obtained in juniper can be mimicked in other cells by adding tannic acid to the fixing solution (Fig. 2.1c). In this way Tilney *et al.* (1973) found that the walls of microtubules from species as diverse as protozoa, echinoderms and birds, all contained 13 subunits. Subsequently a few exceptions with more or less have been found, although always in rather obscure situations.

The freeze-etch technique has also proved useful in the study of microtubule morphology in that it has endorsed most of the observations made after a variety of fixation and staining procedures and negates criticism that these methods produce artefacts. Apart from slight discrepancies in size, it has been found that freeze-etched, and fixed, sectioned and stained microtubules appear similar (Fig. 2.1*d*).

Protofilaments and the microtubule surface lattice   Examination of negatively stained preparations has shown that the walls of microtubules are comprised of linearly ordered protofilaments (Pease, 1963; Fig. 2.3*a*), and it is their profiles that can be seen in sections of microtubules after tannic acid fixation. Although it had proved difficult, if not impossible, to assess the number of protofilaments in a single microtubule from negatively stained preparations, since they usually collapsed and flattened onto the microscope grids, such preparations did allow a side-on view of the microtubule surface. This enabled the width of the protofilaments to be measured (between 3.5–4 nm) and in images of this sort the microtubules appeared beaded, by virtue of a repeat of 8–8.8 nm along their lengths (Fig. 2.3*a*).

The periodicities of flagella microtubules, revealed by negative staining, were analysed using optical diffraction by Grimstone and Klug (1966; Fig. 2.3*b*). From this they observed a 4 nm axial repeat along the protofilaments and a basic surface lattice of 4 x 5 nm units. They also detected additional longitudinal periodicities of 8, 16 and 48 nm which they attributed to perturbations of the simple 4 x 5 nm lattice in the microtubule walls.

Using optical filtering techniques and computer methods of image analysis to reconstruct two- and three-dimensional images from electron micrographs (Fig. 2.3*c*), the 4 x 5 nm subunit surface structure, shown by Grimstone and Klug, was confirmed not only for ciliary and flagellar microtubules, but also for less stable microtubules, such as neurotubules (Chasey, 1972; Amos and Klug, 1974; Erickson, 1974). It became clear too, that the prominent 8 nm periodicity was due not to a zigzag arrangement of subunits, but to an end-to-end alignment of slightly tilted dumb-bell shaped pairs of 4 nm globular units, within the component protofilaments (Fig. 2.3*c*).

The staggering of subunits in adjacent protofilaments gives the appearance of oblique striations across a microtubule, and on the basis of a pitch angle of 15°, and an assumption that there were 12 protofilaments in the microtubule wall, Chasey (1972) concluded that the subunits existed as a four-start helix. As we have already mentioned, however, there are difficulties in interpreting substructure and measuring from negatively stained images of collapsed microtubules, where the front and back protofilaments are

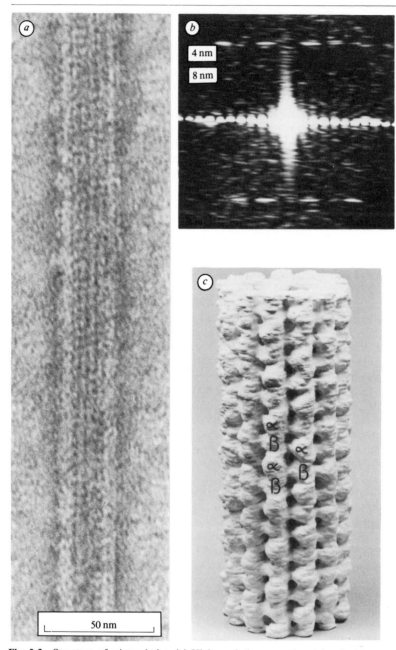

Fig. 2.3 Structure of microtubules. (*a*) High resolution, negative stain, electron

micrograph showing the protofilamentous structure of the microtubule. (*b*) Optical diffraction pattern obtained from the microtubule shown in (*a*), layer lines at 4 and 8 nm are clearly visible. (*c*) Model of a microtubule reconstructed from diffraction data. $\alpha\beta$ tubulin dimers are arranged in a head to tail fashion to form protofilaments. ((*a*) and (*b*) Courtesy of Dr L. A. Amos; (*c*) is from L. A. Amos and A. Klug (1974).)

superimposed. Such problems can be avoided since one occasionally does see instances where a microtubule has split open so that all the protofilaments lie side by side on a grid. Fortuitously there is also a stage during the *in vitro* assembly of microtubules under certain specific conditions (Section 2.2.6) when a flat sheet of protofilaments precedes the formation of a complete microtubule. Preparations of the latter sort have been studied by Erickson (1974) who calculated that since the displacement of one line of subunits, in what would be one helical turn around the cylinder, is 11.3 ± 1.1 nm or roughly three times the 4 nm repeat, then the microtubule structure consists of a three-start helix with each of the three helices having a pitch of 12 nm.

In high resolution studies, Erickson also observed a thin line of stain running down each protofilament and found that optical diffraction patterns showed diffraction spots out to 2.5 nm resolution. He used a computer processing system to reconstruct a filtered and averaged image which showed both the arrangement of the subunits on a model surface lattice and also higher resolution structural details of the individual subunits. The repeating subunit of 4 x 5 nm, which had been thought of as a globular particle, was in fact found to be elongated, skewed at an angle of 40° from the horizontal and apparently divided into two identical halves by a longitudinal cleft.

A few X-ray diffraction studies have been carried out on microtubules (Mandelkow *et al.*, 1977) and these have confirmed much of the data gained from electron microscopy. Although in theory the technique should give better resolution and has the advantage of using unfixed, hydrated material, the considerable technical difficulties encountered in producing the sufficient quantities of oriented material have somewhat limited its application. As these problems are overcome an even more detailed picture of the structure of the microtubule should eventually emerge.

2.1.2 Haloes, arms and cross-links
It is a regular feature of many microtubules, particularly those found in regions of cytoplasmic flow, that they are surrounded by an electron-clear zone or 'halo' which separates them from each other and from other cytoplasmic components (Fig. 2.1*a*). This non-staining area around microtubules was originally thought to be an artefact of fixation, but has been described consistently in differently fixed preparations and also in freeze-etched replicas of microtubules

(Stebbings and Willison, 1973), although no equivalent is seen after negative staining. Attempts to determine the chemical composition of the clear zone using electron microscope cytochemistry have so far been unsuccessful and hence very little is known about its nature except that its existence is dependent upon the integrity of the microtubule itself (Stebbings and Bennett, 1976).

In many instances lateral projections referred to as side-arms appear to extend across the clear zone between the microtubules and particles which move alongside them. In other cases the specific association between microtubules and cytoplasmic particles determined by statistical criteria has been interpreted as indicating that a cross-bridge exists between them, even though such structures are not visualised in the electron microscope (Murphy and Tilney, 1974). Various stains, such as lanthanum and ruthenium red, have on the other hand revealed filamentous elements on the surfaces of axonal microtubules, and the possible significance of these cross-bridges or links will be discussed in subsequent chapters.

In some specialised cases, microtubules are cross-linked together in highly ordered and characteristic patterns. Links of this sort have been observed in situations ranging from cilia and flagella and the axostyles of certain flagellates where the microtubule arrays form motile organelles (see Chapter 3), to the axopodia of heliozoans and the tentacles of suctorian ciliates where they form a structural framework around or within which cytoplasmic particles are transported (see Chapter 5). The links themselves vary in size, length and number in different systems and are associated with a variety of microtubule aggregates, from pairs to complicated spirals. As regards the question of their insertion onto microtubules, there is some evidence that the periodicity which the links often display is related to specific binding sites on the subunits comprising the microtubule surface lattice (McIntosh, 1974). Another possibility is that proteins which form cross-bridges consist of two components, one of which wraps around the microtubule lattice in a specific way and another which projects from the first at regular intervals (Amos, 1977).

2.2   Biochemistry of microtubules

2.2.1 Identification of the microtubule subunit

Although ultrastructural studies have stressed the similarity of microtubules from a wide variety of sources, microtubules serving different cellular functions may differ markedly in their stability, a fact which has greatly influenced the way in which their biochemical characterisation has been approached. Most stable were the outer doublet microtubules of cilia and flagella which could be isolated directly from the cell in reasonable quantity (Chapter 3). These microtubules yielded essentially a single protein with a sedimentation coefficient of 6*S* and a molecular weight of 110,000–120,000 daltons. When denatured in guanidine hydrochloride, however, both these values were halved, suggesting that in aqueous solution the molecule existed as a dimer composed of two 55,000–60,000 dalton monomers. This latter unit was equated with the 4–5 nm structural subunit of the microtubule wall as revealed by negative staining. On the basis of amino acid analysis it was concluded that the protein derived from the outer doublets of cilia and flagella was unique to microtubules and hence designated *tubulin*.

The lability of cytoplasmic microtubules precluded their isolation along similar lines to the microtubules of cilia and flagella. The key to their characterisation proved to be the plant alkaloid colchicine which had long been known as a potent inhibitor of mitosis. Previous suggestions that the disappearance of mitotic spindle fibres (i.e. microtubules) in response to the drug was due to its affinity for the fibre subunit were confirmed by experiments using radioactively labelled colchicine. These showed that the inhibition of mitosis in cultured human cells was due not to the disruption of any metabolic process but rather to the binding of the drug to discrete cellular sites. Colchicine binding was found to be a feature of many types of cells and tissues, but particularly those rich in microtubules (Borisy and Taylor, 1967a). Isolation of the colchicine binding fraction from cell extracts revealed it to be a protein with a sedimentation coefficient of 6*S* and a molecular weight of 110,000 daltons which could be reduced by half in guanidine hydrochloride. Evidence for a direct correlation between colchicine binding and microtubules was provided by experiments in which microtubules constituting the central pair of sperm flagella (Shelanski and Taylor, 1968) and isolated mitotic spindles (Borisy and Taylor, 1967b) were solubilised. In both cases the disappearance of microtubules correlated directly with the appearance in solution of the 6*S* colchicine binding protein. These observations, plus the obvious similarity to the protein extracted from the outer doublets of cilia and flagella, left little doubt that the colchicine binding protein was the microtubule subunit.

2.2.2 The heterodimer model

Early investigations of tubulin derived from the outer doublets of *Tetrahymena* cilia by polyacrylamide gel electrophoresis in the presence of SDS (sodium dodecyl sulphate, a strongly ionic detergent) showed that the protein migrated as a single band. On gels which had been loaded with only small quantities of the same protein, however, two closely spaced bands were distinguished and it was proposed that these had derived from the A and B microtubules of the outer doublet respectively. This interpretation became less likely with the finding that tubulin derived from both cytoplasmic microtubules and the central pair microtubules of *Tetrahymena* cilia were occasionally seen

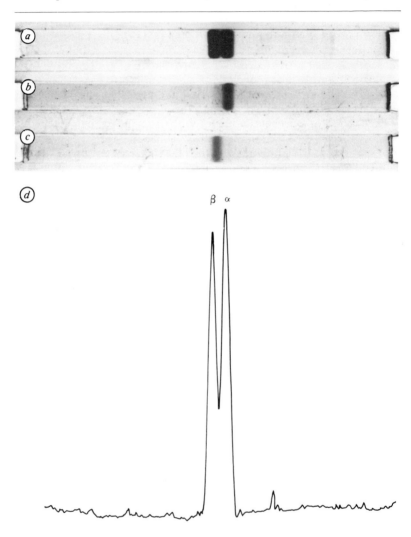

Fig. 2.4 The tubulin heterodimer as revealed by electrophoresis in polyacrylamide gels containing urea. Gel a shows that purified tubulin is resolved as two, closely spaced bands. Gels b and c show the separation of the two components. The densitometer scan of gel a (d) demonstrates the 1:1 ratio of the α and β tubulin monomers. (From J. Bryan and L. Wilson (1971).)

to split into two bands, suggesting rather that microtubules were assembled from heterogeneous subunits. This point was confirmed simultaneously by several workers who showed that tubulin from a variety of sources could be routinely separated into two bands by electrophoresis at alkaline pH on gels containing either urea or urea plus SDS (Bryan and Wilson, 1971; Fig. 2.4). The two bands, designated α and β for the slower and faster migrating components respectively,* exhibited a constant 1:1 ratio and identical molecular weights of 55,000 daltons, their separation being due to difference in net charge. Tryptic peptide and cyanogen bromide mapping, together with amino acid analysis, confirmed that the two subunits were chemically distinct. Since the tubulin dimer is composed of unlike monomers it can be regarded as an $\alpha\beta$ *heterodimer.*

Support for the heterodimer model was forthcoming from experiments in which the outer doublet microtubules of sea urchin sperm flagella were sequentially fractionated with heat and detergent. These revealed an invariant 1:1 ratio of α and β subunits irrespective of how many protofilaments had been solubilised (Meza *et al.*, 1972). This suggested that the distribution of the heterodimer was uniform throughout the wall of the microtubule or in other words that each protofilament was a 'heterofilament' composed of alternating α and β subunits. Conflicting evidence, however, was provided by similar experiments on flagellar microtubules from the unicellular green alga *Chlamydomonas* (Witman *et al.*, 1972). Here it was found that groups of protofilaments resistant to detergent digestion contained only the α subunit although both α and β were obtained in the unfractionated microtubules. These workers therefore proposed a model in which the microtubule was composed of alternating 'homofilaments' consisting of only one type of subunit. The discrepancy between the findings of the different laboratories is probably explained by the fact that at low protein concentrations the α subunit had a greater affinity for the reagents used to stain proteins on polyacrylamide gels than the β (Bibring and Baxandall, 1974). Under these conditions, therefore, preparations containing both subunits would appear to be composed only of the α component.

As a more direct demonstration of its heterogeneity, soluble tubulin was treated with dipropionididate, a compound which chemically cross-links pairs of dimers. If the dimer were composed of like monomers then gel electrophoresis should reveal a mixture of $\alpha\alpha$, $\alpha\beta$ and $\beta\beta$ products. In the event, the linked dimers were predominantly $\alpha\beta$ confirming that soluble tubulin existed largely as a heterodimer.

---

* The reader may come across other terminologies for the two subunits such as A and B, X and Y, 1 and 2. However, the assignation of Greek letters to the dissimilar monomeric units of an oligomer is generally accepted as correct.

Are the α and β tubulin subunits from different sources identical? A comparison of the first 25 amino acid residues at the N-terminus of subunits derived from chick embryo brain and sea urchin sperm outer doublet microtubules revealed that the α chain from each source was identical while the two β chains differed at only one position. These similarities were much greater than those between the α and β subunit from within the same species (Luduena and Woodward, 1973). However, the α and β were identical at 11 of the 25 residues analysed and differences at nine of the remaining positions could be accounted for by a single base change mutation. It is quite possible therefore, that the two subunits have evolved from a common ancestral protein.

The close homology in the primary structure of the two tubulin subunits from such widely diverse sources as the sea urchin and the chick attests to a high degree of conservatism throughout evolution. This conservatism undoubtedly reflects the limited number of permitted alterations in amino acid sequence which would still produce dimers capable of assembling into microtubules. In one case, however, an exception to this argument evidently exists. As we shall see in Chapter 3, the α subunit of the A tubule of sea urchin sperm flagellar outer doublets is distinct from that derived from the B tubule and similarly with the β subunit. However, since the dimers of the B microtubule form a lattice which is quite distinct from that of the A (which in turn is identical to all cytoplasmic microtubules so far examined) a change in the primary structure of the protein is not altogether unexpected.

2.2.3 Nucleotide binding

The ability to bind guanine nucleotides appears to be a general property of microtubules regardless of their source. Tubulin purified from mammalian brain in the absence of guanosine triphosphate (GTP) by an involved procedure lasting several hours still revealed the presence of 0.6–0.8 moles of guanine nucleotide, evidently tightly bound to each 6S dimer (Weisenberg *et al.*, 1968). Protein purified in the presence of GTP and subsequently incubated in ^{3}H-GTP showed a rapid association of radioactivity, suggesting that at least some of the nucleotide bound during preparation was exchangeable with the medium. Each 110,000 g of tubulin can in fact bind 2 moles of nucleotide, one loosely (at the exchangeable or E site of the dimer), the other tightly (at the non-exchangeable or N site).

The role of the nucleotide bound to tubulin remains largely unknown despite a large amount of, often conflicting, evidence. The presence of GTP is apparently important to maintain the native configuration of the molecule as judged by circular dichroism studies and its ability to bind colchicine. Under most of the conditions so far tested, the polymerisation of microtubules *in vitro* (Section 2.2.6) is accompanied by the hydrolysis of GTP at the E site. However, microtubule formation has been observed to proceed, albeit less readily, when either glycerol was substituted for added nucleotide or in the presence of various non-hydrolysable GTP analogues. This latter case is particularly interesting since the microtubules formed are extremely resistant to depolymerisation, possibly indicating that GTP hydrolysis is an important factor in the regulation of microtubule assembly and disassembly. The identification of a specific enzyme, transphosphorylase, which could convert GDP at the N site to GTP using either ATP or GTP as a phosphate donor, raised another possible mechanism whereby microtubule formation could be controlled although the demonstration that tubulin with GDP bound to this site could still polymerise makes this less likely.

2.2.4 Interaction of drugs with microtubule protein

Much of our current understanding of the biochemistry of microtubules derives from the use of a heterogeneous group of compounds loosely referred to as spindle poisons. Cells exposed to such substances are unable to complete mitosis but rather accumulate in a characteristic metaphase in which the chromosomes appear tightly coiled and arranged in various abnormal configurations. With the discovery that certain of these compounds exerted their effect by interacting directly with the microtubule subunit, the spindle poisons became valuable probes of microtubules' structure and function.

Colchicine   An alkaloid derived from the autumn crocus, *Colchicum autumnale*, colchicine is the most extensively studied of the spindle poisons. In addition to being a potent inhibitor of mitosis, colchicine was found to interfere with many other cellular functions involving microtubules, including various forms of cytoplasmic movement, secretion and the maintenance of cell shape. Elucidation of its mechanism of action derived from the introduction of tritium-labelled colchicine which was found to bind specifically to a $6S$, 110,000 molecular weight protein identified as the microtubule subunit in the ratio of 1 mole of colchicine per tubulin dimer (Borisy and Taylor, 1967a, b; Section 2.2.1).

The binding of colchicine to tubulin *in vitro* is slow and temperature dependent but unaffected by pH or ionic strength over a wide range. In a typical experiment, cell extracts were incubated with ^{3}H-colchicine at 37°C for several hours and either passed through a gel filtration column or absorbed onto filters impregnated with DEAE-cellulose to separate the colchicine–tubulin complex from unbound colchicine. Quantification of the binding reaction is complicated by the fact that while formation of the complex is slow, the capacity of tubulin to bind colchicine is unstable and decays rapidly. Once formed at 37°C, however, the tubulin–colchicine complex is extremely stable and the measured binding can be corrected for the instability of the binding site (Wilson, 1975).

In order to understand the interaction of colchicine with microtubules we must first recall briefly that microtubules may vary considerably in their stability. Labile microtubules, including those found in the mitotic spindle and cytoplasm of both plant and animal cells, can be regarded as existing in a delicate equilibrium with their subunits (Inoué and Sato, 1967). When this equilibrium is disturbed by subjecting the cell for instance to high pressure or low temperature, the microtubules rapidly depolymerise. The microtubules of cilia and flagella on the other hand are not disturbed by such treatments and are therefore regarded as stable. Other microtubules may be classified somewhere between these two extremes.

It quickly became clear that the response of microtubules to colchicine depended on their classification into the above scheme. Hence cilia and flagella are unaffected by colchicine while cytoplasmic microtubules rapidly depolymerise in response to low concentrations of the drug. These observations suggested that colchicine could only attach to tubulin when it was in solution and not when it was assembled into microtubules. This point was amply confirmed by experiments using the outer doublet microtubules of sea urchin sperm flagella. Although no colchicine binding to the intact microtubules was detected, soluble tubulin derived from these microtubules bound colchicine in a manner identical to the subunits of their labile cytoplasmic counterparts, i.e. 1 mole of colchicine per mole of tubulin (Wilson and Meza, 1973). Thus the insensitivity of stable microtubules to colchicine is not due to any intrinsic difference in the structure of their subunits, but is merely due to the inaccessibility of the binding site to colchicine once the tubulin dimers are assembled into microtubules. We can therefore summarise the action of colchicine as follows: binding of the drug to soluble tubulin dimers reduces the pool of available subunits, causing a shift in the equilibrium between subunits and microtubules to favour disassembly of the latter. We shall return to this point later on.

The Vinca alkaloids   Like colchicine the *Vinca* alkaloids, vinblastine and vincristine, also cause the reversible disruption of mitotic spindle microtubules (Malawista *et al.*, 1968). The cytoplasm of cells exposed to vinblastine, however, frequently revealed the presence of large, birefringent crystals. In transverse section these appeared to be composed of hexagonally packed cylinders, approximately 28 nm in diameter, forming a network of six-pointed stars (Fig. 2.5a).

Isolation of the crystals from sea urchin eggs showed that they were composed of a 110,000 molecular weight heterodimer which bound both colchicine and guanine nucleotides. Together with amino acid

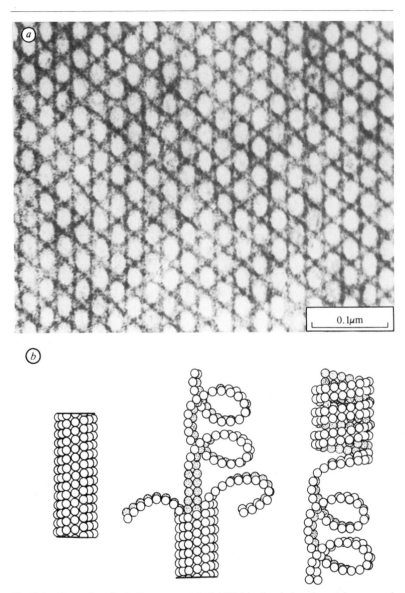

Fig. 2.5 Formation of tubulin paracrystals. (*a*) Vinblastine-induced crystal composed of a meshwork of six-pointed stars. (*b*) Diagram depicting the unwinding of protofilaments from a microtubule and their recoiling to form a larger diameter macrotubule. Lateral aggregation of the latter is thought to result in the formation of the crystal shown in (*a*). ((*a*) Courtesy of Dr D. Starling; (*b*) is from R. K. N. Warfield and G. B. Bouck, (1974).) Copyright 1974 by the American Association for the Advancement of Science.

analysis, these observations suggested that the crystals were composed essentially of pure tubulin complexed to vinblastine.

In addition to the typical crystals, the cytoplasm of cells exposed to vinblastine also occasionally contained large tubules, 34–38 nm in diameter and known as *macrotubules*. Since these structures had also been seen in cells recovering from other treatments known to disrupt microtubules, it was supposed that, like the vinblastine-induced crystals, macrotubules were composed of microtubule protein. This was confirmed by the addition of vinblastine to microtubules assembled *in vitro* (Warfield and Bouck, 1974). Under such conditions pairs of protofilaments were observed to peel away from each end of the microtubule and coil into loose helices. Longitudinal compacting of these spiral structures resulted in the formation of a cylinder with the characteristic macrotubule dimensions (Fig. 2.5*b*).

A very elegant re-examination of the structure of the vinblastine crystal using the tannic acid fixation procedure revealed that the wall of each cylinder of the crystal was similarly composed of helically arranged pairs of protofilaments, although in this case adjacent protofilaments were separated by a distance of 18 nm (Fujiwara and Tilney, 1975). From the similarity between the two structures, together with their frequent close association in cells, it seems probable that crystals are formed by the lateral association of macrotubules through a slight adjustment of the pitch of the coiled protofilaments. What is particularly interesting about these findings, however, is that when arranged helically in a macrotubule or vinblastine-induced crystal, protofilaments of linearly arranged tubulin dimers can bind colchicine but when arranged longitudinally in a microtubule they cannot. Crystals of microtubule protein induced by vinblastine should therefore be extremely valuable in precisely localising the colchicine binding site and in studying the allosteric effects of colchicine binding.

Other spindle poisons   The list of compounds which act either directly or indirectly on microtubule formation is growing continuously. None is as well characterised as colchicine or vinblastine which had the advantage of being in vogue at a time when drug binding was the only 'handle' available for the characterisation of cytoplasmic tubulin. The advent of procedures for studying microtubule formation *in vitro* (Section 2.2.6), however, offers a more direct means of investigating cellular processes involving microtubules and the effort expended in analysing new microtubule inhibitors has decreased accordingly. Despite this, the effects of new compounds are continuously screened in the hope that agents which interrupt different levels of microtubule formation and function will be identified.

Two plant alkaloids, podophyllotoxin and maytansine, have been shown by competition experiments to bind to the colchicine and vinblastine sites on the tubulin dimer respectively. Maytansine is of considerable interest being a potent inhibitor of various forms of tumour and may have chemotherapeutic value in the treatment of leukaemia. Griseofulvin, a metabolite of the fungus *Penicillium*, closely mimicked the antimitotic action of colchicine. The presence of griseofulvin did not interfere with the binding of colchicine, vinblastine or guanine nucleotides so that if it does interact directly with tubulin it does so at a unique site. As yet labelled griseofulvin has not been used to identify the binding site of the drug, but a preliminary analysis of its effect on microtubule polymerisation *in vitro* indicates that it disturbs the interaction of tubulin with the so-called microtubule associated proteins (Section 2.2.6).

Although not strictly a spindle poison, the herbicide isopropyl *N*-phenyl carbamate (IPC) reversibly prevented the reformation of depolymerised microtubules and caused the appearance of multipolar spindles in certain algal cells. Labelled IPC, however, did not bind to tubulin, nor did it block microtubule assembly *in vitro*. The most likely explanation of its antagonistic effect on microtubules appears to be an interaction with the unstructured foci or microtubule organising centres (Section 2.2.5) from which microtubules appear to grow in many plant cells.

2.2.5 Microtubule assembly *in vivo*

In order to explain the effects of colchicine outlined earlier in this chapter we had to consider briefly the concept that certain microtubules exist in a dynamic equilibrium with a pool of subunits. This hypothesis was conceived by Inoué in the early 1950s (a decade before microtubules were actually described in the electron microscope!) on the basis of his observations on the birefringence of living mitotic spindles in marine oocytes. As these cells passed through mitosis, the spindles revealed a conspicuous flickering, an effect Inoué likened to the northern lights and which he interpreted as reflecting the orderly insertion and withdrawal of material in different regions of the spindle (Inoué and Sato, 1967). The birefringent spindle fibres (microtubules) behaved therefore as if they existed in an equilibrium between the polymerised and depolymerised state (Fig. 2.6). Various experimental manipulations confirmed this hypothesis. Exposure of cells to low temperature, high pressure or colchicine resulted in the abolition of spindle birefringence. In each case, however, the spindle reformed when the cell was returned to normal conditions, even when the experiments were performed in the presence of inhibitors of protein synthesis. Hence formation of the spindle could proceed in the absence of *de novo* protein synthesis from a pool of existing subunits.

Although some argument still exists as to whether spindle

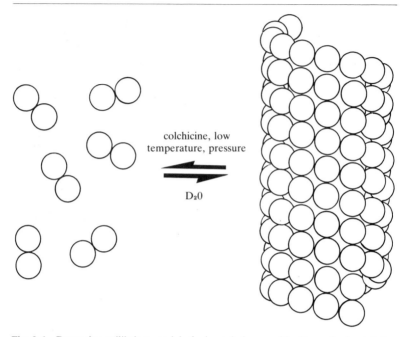

Fig. 2.6 Dynamic equilibrium model of microtubule assembly. Formed microtubules are in equilibrium with their dumbell-shaped subunits. Low temperature, colchicine and hydrostatic pressure favour disassembly of microtubules while heavy water promotes their assembly.

birefringence is due to the presence of microtubules alone, it is generally assumed that changes in birefringence reflect the assembly and disassembly of microtubules. Colchicine which binds to soluble tubulin dimers (Section 2.2.4) therefore exerts its antimitotic action by reducing the number of subunits available for assembly into spindle microtubules, shifting the equilibrium to favour the depolymerised state (Fig. 2.6). By contrast, treatment with heavy water has been shown to augment spindle birefringence (Fig. 2.7). Since D_2O-treated cells frequently contain an increased number of microtubules, these agents apparently shift the equilibrium in the opposite direction, or in other words favour the assembly of microtubules from the subunit pool (Fig. 2.6).

Evidence for the formation of microtubules from a pre-existing pool of subunits has not derived from studies of mitotic spindles alone. Microtubules comprising the axoneme of *Actinosphaerium* could similarly be induced to reversibly assemble and disassemble in the absence of protein synthesis. Likewise the extensive formation of

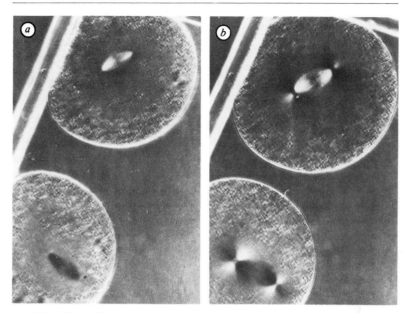

Fig. 2.7 Effect of heavy water on microtubule polymerisation *in vivo*. Oocytes of *Pectinaria* reveal a strongly birefringent spindle when maintained in sea water and viewed in polarised light (*a*). Two minutes after perfusion with 45% D₂O (*b*), the spindles have doubled in volume due to the polymerisation of microtubules from a pool of existing subunits. Three minutes after removal of the D₂O, the spindles return to their original size. (From S. Inoué and H. Sato, (1967).)

microtubules associated with neurite outgrowth during the morphogenetic differentiation of neuroblastoma cells has been shown to involve no change in total cell tubulin concentration.

An equally elegant demonstration of this point was provided by experiments on the regeneration of cilia and flagella. When both flagella were detached from the unicellular green alga *Chlamydomonas*, new flagella regrew after a brief lag. If this experiment was performed in the presence of cycloheximide however, the cell was able to regenerate only two half-length flagella, providing a direct estimation of the size of the pool of flagellar precursors. If only a single flagellum was detached the remaining flagellum shortened until it had reached the same length as its regenerating partner at which point both regrew synchronously to their original length. When the experiment was repeated in the presence of cycloheximide the same sequence of shortening and regrowth was observed. However, under these conditions the total length obtained by the two flagella was equal to the size of the pool (sufficient to grow two half-length flagella) *plus* the length of the undetached flagellum, indicating the subunits derived from the partial disassembly of the latter had been utilised in the formation of its partner (Coyne and Rosenbaum, 1970).

Although assembled from a pool of existing subunits, cilia and flagella are unaffected by treatments which cause the disassembly of cytoplasmic microtubules. In terms of the dynamic equilibrium model therefore, these ciliary and flagellar microtubules may be regarded as stabilised in the polymeric form so that they are no longer depolymerised by the manipulation of subunits in the pool. This stability may be conferred by the interaction of the microtubules with the complex linkages which maintain the $9 + 2$ pattern (Chapter 3). On the other hand the finding that the α tubulin subunit of regenerating *Chlamydomonas* flagella microtubules was specifically phosphorylated may imply that resistance to depolymerisation is conferred through chemical modification of the microtubule protein.

Before we fully understand the formation of microtubules in the cell, the regulation of the pool of tubulin must be understood. Attempts have been made to estimate the amount of tubulin present in cells through the cell cycle either by colchicine binding or quantitative gel electrophoresis of the soluble fraction of cell homogenates. Such experiments have shown that in the eggs and early embryos of *Drosophila* and sea urchins a continuous process of synthesis and breakdown maintains a tubulin pool of approximately constant size. In the latter case the size of the pool which is to form the spindle microtubules may be manipulated by varying the temperature at which the eggs develop.

Total tubulin concentration has been shown to remain virtually constant through the first meiotic division of eggs of the surf clam, *Spissula* (Weisenberg, 1972a). At interphase however, 13% of the colchicine-binding activity of egg homogenates was found to be associated with a particulate fraction which could be sedimented by gentle centrifugation. The amount of particulate tubulin declined during prophase, increased to a maximum at metaphase and declined once again at anaphase. Associated with these fluctuations of colchicine binding was the appearance of an amorphous particle, 10–20 μm in diameter, which was associated with the cell cortex and broken down by treatments which disrupt microtubules. The finding of similar tubulin aggregates in other types of cell suggests that these structures may represent a storage form of tubulin which can be mobilised for assembly into microtubules at the appropriate time.

In this brief consideration of microtubule assembly from existing pools we must mention a situation where this is clearly not the case. The parasite *Naegleria gruberi* exists as an amoeba but can differentiate into a flagellate under starvation conditions – 70% of the tubulin which is assembled into flagella at this transformation is synthesised *de novo*, even though the cell already contains a fiftyfold excess of the protein. By means of radioactive labelling and antibodies directed against flagellar tubulin it was shown that the existing pool was utilised for spindle formation but not for assembly into flagella. These observations demonstrate two points very clearly; first, that not all microtubule formation proceeds from existing subunits and, second, that tubulin synthesised for different functions may not be interchangeable (Fulton and Kowit, 1975).

Nucleation of microtubule formation Microtubule assembly is regulated not only temporarily with respect to other cell cycle events but also spatially, so that microtubules are formed with the correct positioning and orientation. Electron micrographs have shown that microtubules frequently emanate from distinct foci, from which they are assumed to grow. Such structures are generally considered under a single heading of *microtubule organising centres* (MTOCs) although they may vary widely in morphology.

The most obvious MTOCs are basal bodies from which ciliary and flagellar microtubules are derived and centrioles which are the polar organisers of mitotic spindle microtubules in animal cells. Both of these structures are themselves composed of a specialised arrangement of microtubules and therefore could serve directly as a templet for microtubule polymerisation. The spindle poles of many so-called simple organisms, notably the fungi, slime moulds and diatoms, reveal a structurally less well defined category of MTOC, usually referred to as spindle pole bodies. These are multilayered, discoidal structures, frequently inserted into the nuclear membrane and from which spindle microtubules are seen to radiate. The chromosomal kinetochore often exhibits a very similar morphology to these polar organelles and is itself a MTOC for the chromosome to pole microtubules (chromosomal fibres) of the mitotic spindle. A third, yet less well defined class of organising centres is frequently seen in electron micrographs, notably of plant cells, merely as electron-dense amorphous aggregates. At the present time little is known of the composition of these bodies although they are often assumed to contain concentrations of microtubule subunits.

With the development of procedures for studying the formation of microtubules in the test tube (Section 2.2.6) it has been possible to confirm the suggested role of MTOCs in microtubule organisation. In the example shown in Fig. 2.8, microtubules are seen to have polymerised onto one surface of each pair of spindle pole bodies isolated from the yeast *Saccharomyces cerevisiae*. The number of microtubules which grow onto these structures *in vitro* closely corresponds to the number seen to radiate from them in living cells (Hyams and Borisy, 1978). However, spindle pole bodies isolated

41

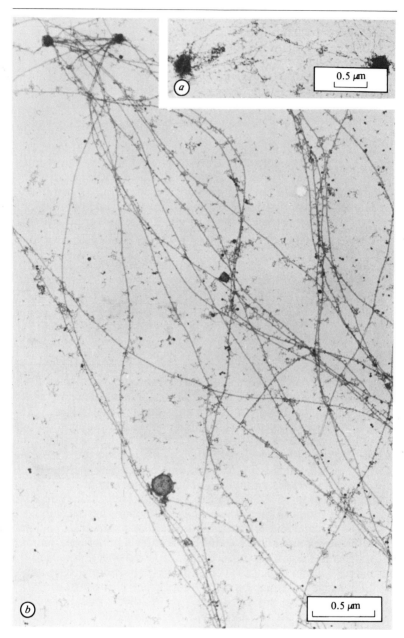

Fig. 2.8 The growth of microtubules onto preformed structures *in vitro*. (*a*) A pair of spindle pole bodies isolated from the yeast *Saccharomyces cerevisiae*. (*b*) The same

structures incubated with microtubule protein purified from porcine brain, showing many long microtubules which have polymerised onto these so-called organising centres. (From J. S. Hyams and G. G. Borisy, *J. Cell Biol.*, (1978).)

from different points in the cell cycle of *S. cerevisiae* differed markedly in their capacity to nucleate the growth of microtubules in this way and it is assumed that changes in the structure or composition of these MTOCs play an important role in determining exactly when and where microtubules are formed within the cell.

2.2.6 Microtubule assembly *in vitro*
Since so many cellular functions involving microtubules were shown to depend upon their ordered assembly and disassembly, many workers began to look for a procedure whereby these events could be studied *in vitro*. The breakthrough in this regard was made by Weisenberg (1972b). He showed that microtubules would form spontaneously in supernatants of brain homogenates at elevated temperatures (37°C) and in the presence of magnesium and GTP, but only if the level of free calcium ions was lowered by the addition of the chelating agent EGTA (ethyleneglycoltetra-acetic acid). Polymerisation was reversible by the addition of colchicine or by cooling to 0°C, treatments known to be disruptive to microtubules in living cells. Cold-depolymerised microtubules revealed the presence of numerous disc-like aggregates or rings with a diameter of 29 ± 4 nm. Removal of these structures by high speed centrifugation left protein which was no longer competent to self-assemble, suggesting that the rings were templets on which microtubules were formed.

Microtubule polymerisation *in vitro* is usually achieved in moderate ionic strength buffer solutions at slightly acidic pH and in the presence of magnesium and GTP, although the precise details vary widely among different laboratories. The formation of microtubules may be monitored by a variety of techniques including electron microscopy, viscometry, turbidity, light scattering and dark-field light microscopy. By various combinations of these methods, polymerisation at 37°C has been shown to involve a short lag, thought to represent the formation of nucleating structures, followed by a rapid increase in the growth of microtubules which is complete after 20–30 minutes. No assembly occurs at protein concentrations below 0.2 mg cm^{-3}, but above this value the amount of polymer formed is proportional to the total protein concentration. This 'critical concentration' possibly reflected the lowest level at which the cooperative association of subunits to form a structure capable of nucleating the growth of a microtubule could occur.

Obviously the nucleating of microtubule assembly is the most interesting event since this determines when and where microtubules

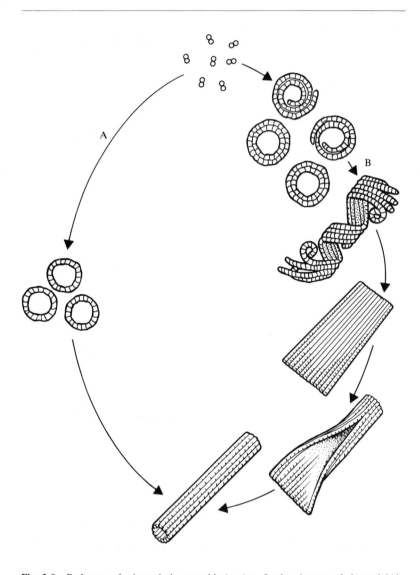

Fig. 2.9 Pathways of microtubule assembly *in vitro*. In the absence of glycerol (A), subunits are first incorporated into disc-shaped aggregates which may serve as templets upon which further addition of subunits occurs. When glycerol is included in the assembly medium (B) a more complex series of intermediates including spirals and sheets of protofilaments can be seen in the electron microscope. (Adapted from J. B. Olmsted *et al.*, *J. Suprmolec. Struct.*, **2,** 429 (1974) and M. W. Kirschner *et al.*, *J. Mol. Biol.*, **99,** 263 (1975).)

are formed in the cell. The finding of rings or discs which might be nucleating structures was rapidly complicated by the discovery of many other tubulin oligomers including double rings, stacks of rings, spirals, sheets of protofilaments and hoops. It quickly became clear that the type of intermediate structures formed *en route* to a microtubule varied with the way the protein was prepared and particularly if glycerol was included during purification, a practice adopted by many workers to obtain increased yields of microtubules.

The pathway of microtubule formation in the presence and absence of glycerol is shown schematically in Fig. 2.9. In the presence of glycerol, double rings and spirals became helical ribbons and then sheets of 13 protofilaments which rolled up to form microtubules. In the absence of glycerol, assembly proceeds via the interaction of subunits to form a templet, the disc or ring, proceeding thereafter by the addition of subunits. Several points must be made about these different schemes. First, glycerol binds irreversibly to tubulin to form a glycerol–tubulin complex which may not represent the state of the molecule in the cell. However, incomplete or 'C'-shaped microtubules, possibly equivalent to the open sheets of protofilaments, are often seen in cells recovering from microtubule depolymerisation. The second point is that thermodynamic analyses of spindle microtubule assembly *in vivo* do not fit closely the condensation–polymerisation model suggested by the non-glycerol scheme. In both cases, however, polymerisation *in vitro* is achieved by a temperature shift between 0° and 37°C, quite obviously not the way microtubule assembly is controlled in the cell.

Microtubule associated proteins   Microtubules purified from brain by the temperature-dependent assembly scheme and examined by polyacrylamide gel electrophoresis were found to be composed of between 75–95% tubulin and 5–25% of a collection of *microtubule associated proteins* (MAPs*). The MAP fraction consisted predominantly of a pair of closely migrating proteins with molecular weights greater than 200,000 daltons plus various minor components which varied with the method of preparation and the source of material. Two lines of evidence suggested that the MAPs were specific microtubule components. The first was the demonstration that they copurified with a constant stoichiometry to tubulin through as many as six cycles of assembly and disassembly (Borisy *et al.*, 1975). The second was the finding that similar proteins were seen to be associated with microtubules isolated directly from brain homogenates by means of the stabilising agent hexylene glycol.

Microtubule protein could be separated into tubulin and MAP

---

* These proteins may also be referred to as HMW for high molecular weight proteins.

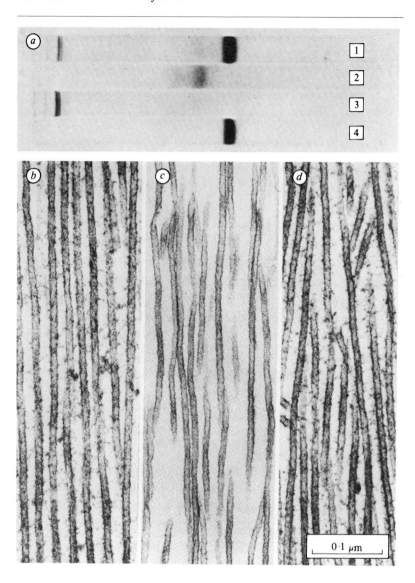

Fig. 2.10 (*a*) Polyacrylamide gels showing the purification of tubulin and MAPs by ion exchange chromatography 1 (Unfractionated microtubule protein purified from porcine brain by *in vitro* assembly and showing both tubulin and a pair of high molecular weight MAPs. 2. Protein eluting in the void volume of the column. 3. and 4. Protein bound to the column and eluted with 0.3 M and 0.8 M KC2 respectively. Tubulin and MAPs are cleanly separated. (*b*) (*c*) and (*d*). Electron micrographs of longitudinal sections through microtubules polymerised from (*b*) unfractionated protein (gel 1. above); (*c*) purified

46

tubulin (gel 3); (*d*) tubulin to which the MAPs have been readded. Removal of the MAPs eliminates the periodic projections from the walls of the microtubules but these are restored when the MAPs are returned. (From D. B. Murphy and G. G. Borisy (1975).)

---

fractions either by gel filtration or ion exchange chromatography. Tubulin purified by the latter procedure (Fig. 2.10) assembled only poorly and was seen in the electron microscope to contain few or no rings. Although this protein could not form microtubules alone, if provided with fragments of preformed microtubules as seeds, extensive polymerisation occurred. When MAP was added back to the purified tubulin, rings were again formed and the ability of the protein to assemble into microtubules was restored (Murphy and Borisy, 1975). These results suggested that the presence of MAP was essential for the initiation of microtubule polymerisation via the formation of rings but thereafter tubulin was competent to continue elongation alone. The identification of a protein which apparently regulated the assembly and disassembly of microtubules in cells was an exciting development and consequently MAP has received considerable attention.

Besides a role in microtubule assembly, sections through microtubules formed in the presence and absence of MAP suggested that these proteins may serve yet another function. Microtubules polymerised from unfractionated material revealed periodic, hair-like projections associated with their surface while those assembled from purified tubulin alone appeared naked and bore no surface material. Readdition of MAP caused this surface component to be restored (Fig. 2.10). As we shall see elsewhere in this book, lateral projections associated with the microtubule surface may serve either as cross-bridges to maintain a precise relationship between adjacent microtubules (this chapter) or as side-arms with a function in motility (Chapter 3). Filamentous material resembling MAP has indeed been observed as elements of axonal microtubules, the source of microtubule protein from which MAP was derived. If it can be unambiguously demonstrated in the future that MAP does in fact represent the surface material associated with microtubules *in situ*, then the biochemical characterisation of these proteins will be enormously important for studies of cytoplasmic microtubules and their role in motility and the determination of cell shape.

More recently, however, two pieces of evidence have seriously challenged the assertion that MAP was a ubiquitous component of cytoplasmic microtubules, specifically involved in the regulation of their assembly. The first was the finding that non-specific, polycationic compounds such as ribonuclease, poly-L-lysine, protamine and DEAE-dextran could substitute for MAP in the stimulation of microtubule polymerisation. While in many cases the microtubules so formed were of abnormal morphology, these results suggested that any substance which could bind to the acidic tubulin dimer would stimulate its assembly *in vitro*. Further, in the presence of high concentrations of magnesium, normal microtubules could be formed from purified tubulin in the absence of any added cofactor.

The second piece of evidence was the non-appearance of MAP in microtubules assembled from sources other than brain, such as tissue culture cells (including certain lines of neuronal origin) and sea urchin eggs. However, the discovery that MAP was associated with microtubules formed from porcine blood platelets may indicate that these proteins are to be found only in non-dividing, non-differentiating tissues where microtubules are not in a continuous process of assembly and disassembly. Further support for this hypothesis is provided by thermodynamic studies of microtubule polymerisation *in vitro* which have shown that the presence of MAP stabilises the microtubule against depolymerisation.

2.3 Identification and morphology of microfilaments

Microfilaments are filamentous structures of about 4–7 nm in diameter, seen in a variety of plant and animal cells, notably in those exhibiting motile phenomena such as amoeboid movement and cytoplasmic streaming. They often occur as parallel bundles (Figs. 2.11 and 2.12), but sometimes also as an anastomosing network, beneath the plasma membrane. When viewed after negative staining, especially where the bundles spread out, microfilaments reveal a double helical morphology with a distinct beaded appearance and an axial repeat of approximately 37 nm (Fig. 2.12*a*).

Microfilaments have been seen in a range of plant cells, and have a similar morphology in, for example, the algae, as in the cells of higher plants. In animal cells, however, the situation is not quite so clear, since in a few instances, in addition to the microfilaments, a class of filaments with a diameter of 10 nm, sometimes called intermediate (because they lie between the thick and thin filaments of muscle), also exist.

Fig. 2.11 Identification of microfilaments in thin sections of mouse 3T3 cells. (*a*) Untreated cell. A single microtubule (arrow) lies adjacent to a bundle of 4–7 nm microfilaments (MF). (*b*) Similar cell but glycerinated and treated with HMM. Microfilaments now reveal the typical barbed appearance. At the bottom of the micrograph a number of intermediate filaments (arrows) which have not been decorated by the HMM are evident. ((*a*) From R. D. Goldman *et al.*, *Exp. Cell Res.*, **90**, 333 (1975); (*b*) is from R. D. Goldman, *J. Histochem. Cytochem.*, **23**, 529 (1975). Copyright 1975 The Histochemical Society.)

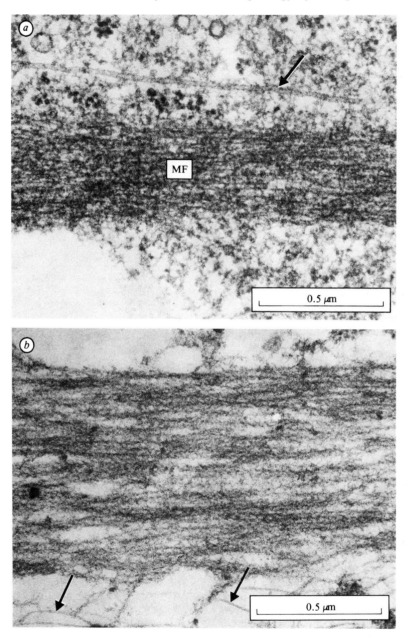

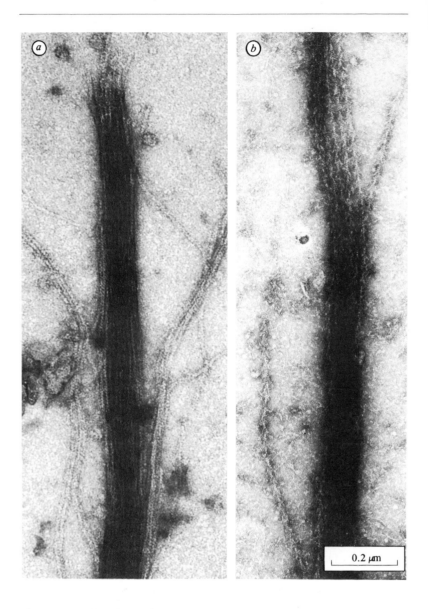

Fig. 2.12 Bundles of microfilaments from the green alga *Nitella* when negatively stained show the typical beaded appearance of polymeric actin (*a*). When incubated with HMM (*b*) the arrowheads all point in the same direction. (From B. A. Palevitz *et al.*, *Proc Nat. Acad. Sci. USA*, **71**, 363 (1974).)

These have been seen, for example, in fibroblasts, muscle cells and glial cells as well as in neurones, where they are known as neurofilaments, and in epithelial cells where they are referred to as tonofilaments. Ten-nanometre filaments are quite distinct from microfilaments and less is known about them, although in contrast to microfilaments it seems unlikely that they are a homogeneous population. Their function is unknown, but it is assumed that they are involved in cell spreading and shape formation, and possibly also in cell locomotion. It should also be mentioned at this point that under certain conditions filaments as large as 16 nm have been observed in several species of amoebae, and the significance of these is discussed in the chapter devoted to amoeboid movement.

As readers will have appreciated already, there is a striking similarity between the morphology of a microfilament and the thin F-actin filament of striated muscle (Chapter 1). Indeed, the identity of, and homology between, microfilaments in different plant and animal cells has been investigated extensively using two different approaches derived directly from studies of muscle. The first has been the specific decoration of microfilaments with heavy meromyosin and the second, their visualisation by immunofluorescence using antibody directed against skeletal muscle actin.

2.3.1 Heavy meromyosin binding to microfilaments

In his studies of the interaction between actin and myosin in muscle (Chapter 1), Huxley showed that isolated actin filaments formed arrowhead-type complexes when treated with HMM. The formation of arrowhead complexes, which are dissociated in the presence of ATP, has subsequently become regarded as a definitive test for the identification of polymerised actin. Since then Huxley's technique has been adapted by Ishikawa *et al.* (1969) who observed the characteristic arrowhead configurations in sections of a variety of non-muscle cells including fibroblasts, chondrogenic cells, nerve cells and several types of epithelial cells (Figs. 2.11*b* and 2.12*b*). The binding of HMM within these cells was specifically to microfilaments and no interaction occurred between HMM and other cell components, including 10 nm filaments and microtubules. Furthermore, the periodicity of the HMM binding and its reversibility by the addition of ATP was identical to that seen with the thin filament of the myofibril.

The HMM labelling technique has subsequently received an enormous amount of attention and decorated actin filaments have been reported in many cell types in numerous organisms. One slightly worrying aspect of such studies, however, is that although microfilaments are routinely identified in HMM treated cells, in untreated controls they are often conspicuous by their absence. Two possible explanations, both supported by experimental observations, have been proposed to explain this anomaly. The first is that microfilaments in the absence of HMM are not well preserved by conventional fixation procedures and hence are lost during the preparation of the cell for electron microscopy. The second possibility is that treatment with HMM actually induces the formation of filaments from concentrations of monomeric subunits. The latter possibility has caused many workers to regard the localisation of microfilaments at a particular site in the cell by the HMM procedure with some reservation (Tilney, 1975).

2.3.2 Visualisation of microfilaments by immunofluorescence

As an alternative to their identification by electron microscopy, microfilaments, like microtubules, can also be visualised by immunofluorescence. For many years actin had been regarded as a non-antigenic protein, the rationalisation for this view being that since actin is present in essentially identical form in probably every type of cell, the production of antibodies against it would be self-destructive. However, in a series of experiments which were to have a fairly momentous impact, Lazarides and Weber (1974) found that actin recovered from SDS–polyacrylamide gels, and hence denatured, could be used to raise antisera. As with antibody directed against microtubule protein (Section 2.1), fluorescent antiactin decorated an elaborate, yet distinct, system of intracellular fibres in fibroblasts (cf. Fig. 2.2*b* with 2.2*a*). Bundles of microfilaments were seen to run parallel to each other and to the long axis of the cell, an arrangement apparently identical to the so-called 'stress fibres' previously described in such cells by phase contrast microscopy (see also Fig. 4.12). That these structures were indeed microfilaments was confirmed by another ingenious trick using fluorescein-conjugated HMM (Sanger, 1975) which revealed a similar system of fluorescent fibres.

The great advantage of these procedures is not only that they allow the whole cellular organisation of microfilaments to be visualised within a single field of view but that they also allow changes in this distribution through the cell cycle to be readily monitored.

2.4 Biochemistry of microfilaments

Structural studies have conclusively and comprehensively demonstrated, on the basis of their size, morphology and specific interaction with HMM, that microfilaments are composed of the muscle protein *actin*. Inevitably, this finding has prompted speculation that the function of microfilaments in non-muscle cells can be equated to that of the thin filament of striated muscle, that is that they undergo some sort of cyclic interaction with myosin which results in the conversion of chemical energy into movement. Although such an analogy is obviously extremely tempting, the differences between the two situations should first be carefully considered before we allow such conclusions to irreversibly bias our judgement. In muscle, thin, actin filaments are organised in a precise relationship to thick, myosin filaments to form a stable and highly ordered contractile unit, the sarcomere. In non-muscle cells myosin can rarely be visualised in the electron microscope. Is myosin in fact present in such cells and, if so, how is it organised with respect to the microfilaments? Is the interaction between the two components controlled by calcium via a system analogous to the troponin–tropomyosin complex of muscle? Many non-muscle cells are dynamic structures constantly undergoing changes in shape and internal organisation. In contrast to the thin filaments of muscle therefore, microfilaments are often transient structures being constantly formed and broken down. How is this assembly and disassembly controlled? What supplies the positional information to ensure that microfilaments are formed at the correct site in the cell? Do these special properties of microfilaments in non-muscle cells mean that cytoplasmic actin and myosin are biochemically different from their muscle counterpart?

Such questions have stimulated an intensive effort designed to identify and characterise the so-called 'contractile' proteins from cells other than muscle. These studies can be clearly traced back to the pioneering work of Loewy (1952) who showed that crude cytoplasmic extracts obtained from the plasmodia of a primitive and unspecialised organism, the myxomycete *Physarum polycephalum* (Chapter 4), possessed certain properties reminiscent of muscle actomyosin. Loewy's findings lay dormant for a decade until two groups of workers independently demonstrated that such heterogeneous *Physarum* extracts contained proteins which could be unambiguously identified as actin and myosin (Hatano and Oosawa, 1966; Adelman and Taylor, 1969). The results of the intensive research effort stimulated by these findings are described briefly in the following sections.

2.4.1 Cytoplasmic contractile proteins
Actin   Actin has already been demonstrated in animal cells, both vertebrates and invertebrates, plants, protozoa and fungi and it seems likely that it will eventually be shown to be a ubiquitous component of all living organisms. Often, indeed, actin appears to be the single most common cellular protein and estimates have suggested that it may constitute up to a remarkable 10–20% of the total protein of such cells as protozoa, slime moulds, blood platelets and nervous tissue. The abundance of this protein, equivalent to a cellular concentration in the region of $10\ \mathrm{mg\ cm^{-3}}$, strongly suggests that it is extremely important to cell function.

Actin isolated from all non-muscle cells (to date about 50 types of cell have been analysed) reveals a similar molecular weight (about 42,000 daltons) and amino acid composition to muscle actin although only the latter has been completely sequenced. Slight but important differences have however been noted and these are probably reflected in the altered biochemical properties of cytoplasmic actins. Deciphering these differences probably holds the key to understanding the function of actin and its interaction with myosin in widely different types of cell.

Partial amino acid analysis of actins from different tissues of the same organisms (e.g. human heart and human blood platelets) shows differences in their primary sequence. Evidently therefore these molecules are coded by different genes and quite clearly this may explain how the synthesis of the correct form of actin in a particular tissue is regulated. All actin molecules so far examined contain one residue of the unusual amino acid N^{τ}-methylhistidine which has proved to be a useful marker for facilitating the identification of actin in cell extracts.

Actin from all sources polymerises into characteristic double helical filaments upon alteration of the ionic strength of the environment. Such filaments bind reversibly to both muscle myosin and the proteolytic fragments HMM and S1, and cause a stimulation of myosin ATPase activity. This ability to undergo a cyclic interaction with myosin obviously suggests a way in which microfilaments may be involved in the generation of force for cell movement. Not all actins, however, stimulate the enzymatic activity of myosin to an equivalent degree. Actin from *Acanthamoeba*, for example, is fairly inefficient in this regard and this might well reflect the low levels of force generation necessary for movement of this protozoan in contrast to the massive energy output of muscle.

Myosin   The characterisation of cytoplasmic myosin has proved to be a less tractable problem than has so far proved to be the case for actin. Like actin, myosin is widely distributed among a variety of different cell types but is present in much lower concentrations (often in the order of one-hundredth the actin concentration) and in some specialised cells may be absent altogether (Section 4.1). Like its muscle equivalent, cytoplasmic myosin has three characteristic properties:

1.   It binds reversibly to actin filaments.
2.   It possesses an actin-activated ATPase activity.
3.   It forms filaments under physiological conditions.

Each of these characteristics carries the hidden implication that cytoplasmic myosin is involved in the generation of force cell motility.

Although limited, available information on cytoplasmic myosin has shown that, unlike actin which has been highly conserved throughout evolution, myosin from different sources may exhibit notable differences in its chemical and physical properties. In most cases however, cytoplasmic myosins resemble the corresponding protein from muscle in molecular weight (roughly 470,000 daltons), in the fact that they are composed of heavy and light chains and form bipolar filaments. The most obvious exception to this generalisation is revealed by myosin extracted from the soil amoeba, *Acanthamoeba castellanii*. This organism has been extensively used in studies of cytoplasmic actin and myosin, partly because it is primitive and unspecialised but also because it can be grown in the large quantities demanded by such experiments. *Acanthamoeba* myosin has a much lower molecular weight (approximately 180,000 daltons) and is composed of one heavy and two light chains of molecular weight 140,000, 16,000 and 14,000 daltons respectively. This myosin fails to form filaments *in vitro* but its interaction with microfilaments is strongly indicated by the finding that this small protein will induce the lateral aggregation of actin filaments from muscle (Pollard, 1975).

An important contribution to the localisation of myosin in cultured human cells was provided by the very diligent studies of Fujiwara and Pollard (1976). These workers demonstrated that fluorescent-labelled myosin antibody decorated the same system of intracellular fibres previously identified as microfilaments (Section 2.3.2; Fig. 2.2*b*), albeit in a slightly different manner. While actin antibody produced a continuous staining along the fibres, myosin antibody was visualised as a periodic system of dots. Ideally one would like to see these observations confirmed by some other procedure such as electron microscopy before the localisation of myosin along these microfilament bundles is accepted uncritically. Until this is possible we must assume that myosin in the cell is associated in a very specific way with actin (micro) filaments.

Cofactor   Although the ATPase activity of all cytoplasmic myosins is activated by actin, the extent of this activation is low, two to fivefold, in comparison to the fiftyfold plus stimulation observed in the case of the same proteins from muscle. In *Acanthamoeba*, no actin-activated myosin ATPase is detected unless another protein, also isolated from cytoplasmic extracts and having a molecular weight of approximately 100,000 daltons, is added. In the presence of this third protein, known as *cofactor*, the stimulation of myosin enzymatic activity is seen to be approximately equivalent to the high levels previously seen only in the case of muscle myosin. A similar situation has also been seen to exist in the case of myosin from rabbit alveolar macrophages, although as yet the cofactor has not been purified so we do not know if it is the same protein found in *Acanthamoeba*. Although this evidence is very preliminary, cofactors may eventually be shown to be extremely important in the regulation of actin–myosin interactions during cell motility.

Troponin–tropomyosin   Despite some structural information, based upon the immunofluorescence technique, which suggests that tropomyosin is associated with the microfilament bundles of cultured fibroblasts (Section 2.3.2), the biochemical evidence for the presence of these regulatory proteins in other cells is fragmentary. Tropomyosin has been convincingly demonstrated in blood platelets and brain tissue but virtually no information is available regarding the distribution of troponin. In primitive systems such as certain invertebrates and protozoa, the lack of calcium sensitivity of the isolated contractile proteins may be interpreted as providing circumstantial evidence for the absence of these regulatory molecules.

2.4.2 Gelation of cytoplasmic extracts

As an alternative to the classical biochemical descriptions of purified actin, myosin and accessory proteins, described briefly above, the cooperative interaction of these molecules and their role in cell motility may also be investigated in crude cytoplasmic extracts. Such a system has the advantage that all the force-generating elements of the cell, some of which would inevitably be lost during purification of the more obvious components, will be present, although this is counterbalanced to some extent by the fact that such extracts will also contain many extraneous proteins not involved in cell movement. The use of cell extracts to investigate the association of cellular contractile proteins was inspired by the experiments of Kane (1974, 1976). He found that when homogenates of sea urchin eggs, prepared in the cold in the presence of ATP and centrifuged at high speed to remove all particulate matter, were warmed to 35–40°C, a gel of actin filaments was formed. If allowed to remain longer at the elevated temperature, the gel further contracted to form a solid pellet.

This observation was particularly exciting since the gelation of the cytoplasmic extract appeared to mimic the sol–gel transformation which takes place in the cytoplasm of cells such as amoebae and confirms the findings of many early cytologists who noted the effect of temperature on cytoplasmic consistency. Analysis of the gelled sea urchin extract by SDS–gel electrophoresis revealed the presence of actin as the major component of the gel plus two other proteins with molecular weights of 58,000 and 220,000 daltons respectively. If fractions containing the latter were added to purified F-actin from urchin eggs, the mixture again rapidly gelled. In the electron microscope it could be seen that the actin filaments formed highly

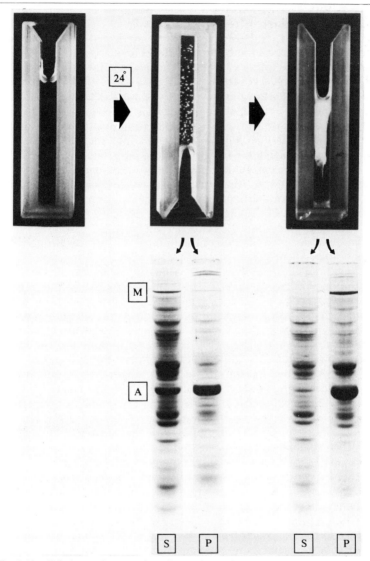

Fig. 2.13 Gelation and contraction of *Acanthamoeba* cytoplasmic extracts. Homogenates of amoebae were centrifuged at 100,00 x *g* for 60 minutes and allowed to warm to room temperature. Within 20–30 minutes the extract had gelled (middle cuvette) and, if left longer, eventually contracted (cuvette on the right). Both the gel and the contracted gel were centrifuged and the resulting pellets (P) and supernatants (S) analysed by polyacrylamide gel electrophoresis. Actin (A) is the major component of the gelled extract but upon contraction it becomes associated with myosin (M) and an unidentified 50,000 dalton protein. (From T. D. Pollard (1975).)

ordered, paracrystalline arrays, presumably maintained in this pattern by these copurifying proteins.

Kane's findings have subsequently been confirmed by several other workers using various kinds of cells. *Acanthamoeba* extracts left at room temperature for 20–30 minutes formed a gel which would not pour from an inverted cuvette (Fig. 2.13; Pollard, 1976). As with the egg extract, if left to stand further the gel eventually contracted into an opaque pellet. By electrophoresis the gel was once again shown to be composed largely of actin plus some other minor proteins including one of approximately 50,000 daltons and a high molecular weight species greater than 200,000 daltons. The contracted gel on the other hand revealed a markedly different composition, containing in addition to actin and the 50,000 molecular weight component, myosin and myosin cofactor. Perhaps most interestingly, contraction of the gel was also found to be dependent upon the presence of low levels $(10^{-7}–10^{-6}$ M) of calcium (Pollard, 1976).

The biphasic gelation and contraction of cell extracts strongly suggests that microfilaments serve a dual role in cell function. First, contraction of the *Acanthamoeba* cytoplasm has confirmed that the interaction of microfilaments with myosin and cofactor is responsible for the generation of force for the movement of the cell and, further, that this interaction is regulated by calcium. Second, the lateral cross-bridging of microfilaments by other specific proteins appears to serve a cytoskeletal role in cytoplasmic organisation, possibly determining regions of different viscosity, most notably at the cell cortex. This latter interpretation is strongly supported by observations on a motile system of a very different kind. The acrosomal reaction of certain echinoderm sperm is described in some detail in Chapter 4. Here it is sufficient to note that the sperm of the horseshoe crab *Limulus* discharge a process composed of tightly packed bundles of microfilaments which can be isolated for analysis by electrophoresis (Tilney, 1975). This has shown that the microfilament bundle is held together by two proteins, one of which has a molecular weight of 55,000 daltons. Since the formation of tightly packed bundles is characteristic of microfilaments in both plant and animal cells (e.g. Figs. 2.11 and 2.12) it seems possible that a protein or family of proteins in the molecular weight range of 50,000–60,000 daltons is responsible for maintaining this important spatial distribution of filaments.

2.4.3 Actin–membrane associations and the storage of actin in the cell

In the preceding section we described how cross-linked microfilaments could form a gel analogous to the viscous layer of cortical ectoplasm found in many cells. The association of microfilaments with the cell cortex is amply corroborated by extensive electron microscopic observations which have shown that microfilaments are often conspicuously localised beneath the plasmalemma. In addition to this direct evidence, the argument can also be made on purely functional considerations. In the case of cells which move across a substratum, for example, force generated within the cell is of necessity transmitted through the plasmalemma and in other situations, to be discussed later, distortions of the plasmalemma by microfilaments are manifested by gross changes in cell shape.

Possibly the most extensive biochemical investigation of the association of actin with the cell membrane has centred upon the proteins of the human red blood cell ghost. The erythrocyte ghost (i.e. isolated membrane) can be obtained with great purity and in large quantities and is widely used as a model system in studies of membrane molecular biology (Steck, 1974). Extraction of purified ghosts with 0.1 mM EDTA (ethylenediaminetetra-acetic acid, a powerful chelator of divalent cations) yields three proteins, one of which comigrates on SDS–polyacrylamide gels with muscle actin, plus two others with molecular weights greater than 200,000 daltons. The latter two proteins, which are collectively referred to as *spectrin*, compose some 20–25% of the erythrocyte membrane and are thought to be involved in regulating the lateral movements within its fluid structure.

If EDTA extracts are treated with myosin fragment S1, typical arrowhead-decorated filaments are formed, demonstrating that the smaller of the three proteins is in fact actin. Electron microscopy, either by thin sections or negative staining, however, failed to reveal any filaments associated with the untreated ghosts although their inner, cytoplasmic surface revealed an amorphous, 'fuzzy' layer (Tilney and Detmers, 1975). Hence actin is present in the erythrocyte membrane, evidently in an unpolymerised state, and when it is extracted it is always accompanied by two proteins integral to the structure of the membrane. That the association with spectrin is responsible for maintaining actin in the monomeric form, is suggested by two pieces of indirect evidence. First, treatment of ghosts with trypsin, to which spectrin but not actin is extremely sensitive, results in the polymerisation of actin into filaments. Second, addition of the EDTA extract containing spectrin to G-actin prepared from skeletal muscle effectively inhibited its G–F transformation (Tilney and Detmers, 1975).

Although based largely on circumstantial evidence, the assumption that the association of actin with spectrin determines its localisation at the cell surface has found support from an elegant series of experiments on a very different system. The acrosomal reaction of sperm of the sea cucumber, *Thyone*, is described in some detail in Chapter 4. Like that of *Limulus* (Section 2.4.2), the acrosomal process in this animal is also composed of a tightly packed bundle of

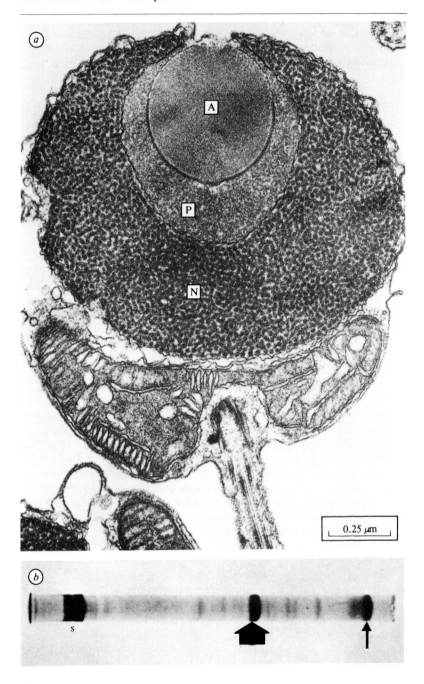

Fig. 2.14 Section through a spermatozoan of *Thyone*. (*a*) The acrosome (A) and periacrosomal material (P) lie in an indentation of the nucleus (N). (*b*) Polyacrylamide gel of purified periacrosomal material. The gel shows three prominent bands, actin (large arrow) plus two high molecular weight 'spectrin-like' proteins (s). The small arrow marks the position of the dye front. ((*a*) From L. G. Tilney (1976a); (*b*) from L. G. Tilney (1976b).)

microfilaments (Tilney, 1976a, b). In this case, however, the filaments are formed by the explosive polymerisation of a pool of amorphous material, presumably monomeric actin, closely resembling the fuzzy inner surface of the erythrocyte ghost. This *periacrosomal material* occupies a cup-shaped region around the acrosomal vesicle, the two lying in an indentation of the sperm nucleus (Fig. 2.14*a*). When *Thyone* sperm were demembranated under conditions of low ionic strength and slightly acidic pH, the sperm nuclei to which the periacrosomal material remained attached were cleanly isolated. Treatment of the nuclei with DNase digested away the chromatin allowing the 'sperm cups', i.e. the periacrosomal material, to float free. The fact that the cups maintained their integrity despite not being enclosed in a vesicle or vacuole implied that the actin must be bound in some way to prevent its diffusion.

Analysis of the isolated sperm cups by SDS–polyacrylamide gel electrophoresis revealed that the periacrosomal material was composed, like the EDTA extract of the erythrocyte ghost, of three proteins (Fig. 2.14*b*). The major component, as suspected, was actin but two high molecular weight proteins closely resembling spectrin were also resolved. Exposure of the cups either to trypsin or to conditions of alkaline pH and high ionic strength dissociated these 'spectrin-like' molecules from actin which rapidly became soluble and hence competent to polymerise *in vitro* into characteristic double helical filaments. Tilney (1975) has proposed that the periacrosomal material represents a storage form of actin which is maintained in a non-polymerisable, non-diffusible state by association with the two high molecular weight proteins. Prior to the acrosomal reaction of the sperm, dissociation of actin from these two associated proteins converts it to the more familiar G (monomeric) state which can rapidly polymerise into filaments. This sequence can be detailed as follows:

Profilamentous actin → G-actin → F-actin

A good deal more rigorous biochemical analysis is required to establish unambiguously that this sequence is correct and in particular to define the relationship between the high molecular weight proteins from the two systems. The findings do, however, offer an attractive explanation of how a pool of existing actin subunits could be rapidly mobilised for polymerisation into filaments.

One unanswered question regarding the periacrosomal material of *Thyone* spermatozoa is, how does this monomeric actin become localised in one particular region of the cell when it is continuous with the rest of the cytoplasm and not partitioned from it by a membrane? A clue to the answer is provided by examination of the structure of the sperm head (Fig. 2.14*a*). This reveals that the portion of the apical acrosomal vesicle in contact with the periacrosomal material is morphologically distinguishable from the remainder of the membrane in that it is significantly thicker than a typical unit membrane structure. Similarly it can be seen that the nuclear envelope bounding the sperm cup is also specialised, in this case the inner and outer membranes have fused. When sperm were disrupted by hypotonic shock, the periacrosomal material remained firmly attached to either or both of these specialised membrane regions which appeared to be more resistant to solubilisation by either detergent or glycerol treatment than the remaining membrane system of the cell. These observations further emphasise the already stated hypothesis, that the localisation of cellular actin may depend on its specific interaction with the cell membrane.

In addition to the actin-membrane interactions detailed above, electron microscopy has clearly shown that the plasmalemma can also serve as a site for the attachment of microfilaments. This is particularly evident in the case of the stress fibres of cultured fibroblasts and the microfilament bundles of intestinal brush border cells where large numbers of microfilaments are seen to extend from densely-staining, differentiated, membrane foci (Chapter 4). The membrane in these cases can be thought of as being analogous to the Z line of the sarcomere, to which the thin filaments of the myofibril are firmly anchored and through which force generated by sliding between thick and thin filaments is imparted. If the analogy is continued further, one would predict that the decoration of microfilaments attached to membranes with HMM or S1 would reveal arrowheads of uniform polarity pointing away from their site of anchorage as has been so conclusively demonstrated in muscle (Section 1.3). Although such experiments present considerable technical difficulties, results so far obtained support the prediction that discrete regions of the cell membrane serve as specific sites for the directed assembly of microfilaments.

2.4.4 Cytochalasin B
The demonstration that the plant alkaloid colchicine disrupted many cellular processes involving microtubules by its specific interaction with the tubulin subunit prompted many workers to search enviously for a compound which would exert an equally potent effect upon microfilaments. To many, the search appeared to be over with the

discovery that a class of compounds, the *cytochalasins*, isolated from the culture fluids of certain moulds, quickly and reversibly inhibited locomotion and cytokinesis in a variety of mammalian cells in culture (Carter, 1967). One of these compounds, *cytochalasin B*, derived from the fungus, *Helminthosporium dematioideum*, has subsequently been extensively used as a cytological probe of microfilament function although the interpretation of its mode of action has been the subject of continued, and often acrimonious, debate (Estensen *et al.*, 1971).

Inspired by the observation that the application of cytochalasin B to dividing marine eggs resulted in the disappearance of the band of microfilaments underlying the cleavage furrow (the contractile ring, Chapter 6), Wessells *et al.* (1971) investigated its effect upon a variety of morphogenetic and locomotory cell movements. In such diverse examples as the differentiation of epithelial tissue, elongation of axons of embryonic nerve cells, migration of single cells in culture and streaming in plant cells, movement was found to be reversibly inhibited by exposure to low levels ($0.5-30\,\mu$g cm^{-3}) of cytochalasin. In most cases, electron microscopy of treated cells revealed that the cessation of movement was accompanied by the breakdown of microfilaments which were replaced by aggregates of granular material. On the basis of such observations, these workers made the rather bold assertion that cytochalasin B caused the specific disruption of the microfilamentous contractile system of cells (Wessells *et al.*, 1971).

Subsequent work on the activity of cytochalasin has however indicated that a more circumspect evaluation of its effect is desirable (Burnside and Manasek, 1972; Carter, 1972). This was suggested largely on the basis of a further examination of its action upon cell cleavage in both mouse L cells and *Xenopus* eggs. In both cases, doses of cytochalasin sufficient to block cytokinesis in fact allowed furrowing to commence normally, although later the cleavage furrow regressed, and caused no visible disruption of the contractile ring microfilaments. Subsequently, microfilaments in many other situations were shown to be similarly resistant to the inhibitory effect of cytochalasin B.

Studies on the interaction of cytochalasin B with purified skeletal muscle actin and myosin *in vitro* have failed to resolve these conflicting observations. Using electron microscopy as an assay, Forer *et al.* (1972) demonstrated that cytochalasin inhibited neither the polymerisation of actin into filaments nor the reversible decoration of such filaments with HMM. Completely contrary to these findings however, other workers have shown by viscometry that cytochalasin B *did* block both the polymerisation of actin and its activation of the ATPase activity of HMM, although in this latter case it should be stressed that the concentration of cytochalasin employed was greatly in excess of that required to inhibit the movement of living cells

63

(Spudich and Lin, 1972).

Perhaps a partial explanation of the controversy was supplied by the finding that, in addition to the effects previously noted, cytochalasin B also inhibits the incorporation of exogenous sugars by a variety of cells, presumably by its interaction with the cell membrane. Bearing in mind the emphasis we placed earlier upon the association between microfilaments and membranes it is not inconceivable that the disruption of the former is a secondary consequence of the disturbance of membrane integrity by cytochalasin. The hydrophobic nature of the compound might further indicate that such a mechanism is indeed possible. Unfortunately, although ^{3}H-cytochalasin is available and potentially could resolve this question, it has yet to be shown what its target site is within the cell or even if it enters the cell at all.

A more recent and perhaps more direct approach towards resolving some of this contradictory evidence has exploited the temperature-dependent gelation phenomena of cell extracts (Section 2.4.2). In the case of both rabbit pulmonary macrophages and HeLa cells, cytochalasin inhibited the gelation of crude extracts by dissociating actin filaments from the accessory proteins responsible for maintenance of the gel, while having no effect on the filaments themselves (Weihing, 1976; Hartwig and Stossel, 1976). Although these results are encouraging for supporters of a cytochalasin–microfilament interaction, they are still preliminary and the interpretation of the effect of cytochalasin B on living cells must still be approached with an open mind.

Suggestions for further reading and references

Further reading

CLARKE, M. and SPUDICH, J. A. (1977) Nonmuscle contractile proteins: the role of actin and myosin in cell motility and shape determination, *Ann. Rev. Biochem.*, **46**, 797–822.

HEPLER, P. K. and PALEVITZ, B. A. (1974) Microtubules and microfilaments, *Ann. Rev. Plant Physiol.*, **25**, 309–62.

HITCHCOCK, S. E. (1977) Regulation of motility in non-muscle cells, *J. Cell Biol.*, **74**, 1–15.

OLMSTED, J. B. and BORISY, G. G. (1973) Microtubules, *Ann. Rev. Biochem.*, **42**, 507–40.

POLLARD, T. D. and WEIHING, R. R. (1974) Actin and myosin and cell movement. *CRC Crit. Revs. Biochem.*, **2**, 1–65.

ROBERTS, K. (1972) Cytoplasmic microtubules and their functions, *Progr. Biophys. Mol. Biol.*, **28**, 371–420.

SNYDER, J. A. and McINTOSH, J. R. (1976) Biochemistry and physiology of microtubules, *Ann. Rev. Biochem.*, **45**, 699–720.

STEPHENS, R. E. and EDDS, K. T. (1976) Microtubules: Structure chemistry and function, *Physiol. Revs.*, **56**, 709–77.

References

ADELMAN, M. R. and TAYLOR, E. W. (1969) Isolation of an actomyosin protein complex from slime mould plasmodium and the separation of the complex in actin- and myosin-like fractions, *Biochemistry,* **8,** 4964–75.

AMOS, L. (1977) Arrangement of high molecular weight associated proteins on purified mammalian brain microtubules, *J. Cell Biol.,* **72,** 642–54.

AMOS, L. A. and KLUG, A. (1974) Arrangement of subunits in flagellar microtubules, *J. Cell Sci.,* **14,** 523–49.

BIBRING, T. and BAXANDALL, J. (1974) Tubulins 1 and 2. Failure of quantitation in polyacrylamide gel electrophoresis may influence their identification. *Exp. Cell Res.,* **86,** 120–6.

BORISY, G. G., MARCUM, J. M., OLMSTED, J. B., MURPHY, D. B. and JOHNSON, K. A. (1975) Purification of tubulin and associated high molecular weight proteins from porcine brain and characterization of microtubule assembly *in vitro, Ann. N.Y. Acad. Sci.,* **253,** 107–32.

BORISY, G. G. and TAYLOR, E. W. (1967a) The mechanism of action of colchicine. Binding of colchicine-³H to cellular protein, *J. Cell Biol.,* **34,** 525–33.

BORISY, G. G. and TAYLOR, E. W. (1967b) The mechanism of action of colchicine. Colchicine binding to sea urchin eggs and the mitotic apparatus, *J. Cell Biol.,* **34,** 535–48.

BRYAN, J. and WILSON, L. (1971) Are cytoplasmic microtubules heteropolymers? *Proc. Natl. Acad. Sci. USA,* **68,** 1762–6.

BURNSIDE, B. and MANASEK, F. J. (1972) Cytochalasin B: problems in interpreting its effect on cells, *Dev. Biol.,* **27,** 443–4.

CARTER, S. B. (1967) Effects of cytochalasins on mammalian cells, *Nature,* **213,** 261–4.

CARTER, S. B. (1972) The cytochalasins as research tools in cytology, *Endeavour,* **31,** 77–82.

CHASEY, D. (1972) Subunit arrangement in ciliary microtubules in *Tetrahymena pyriformis, Exp. Cell Res.,* **74,** 140–6.

COYNE, B. and ROSENBAUM, J. L. (1970) Flagellar elongation and shortening in *Chlamydomonas.* II. Reutilization of flagellar proteins, *J. Cell Biol.,* **47,** 777–81.

ERICKSON, H. P. (1974) Microtubule surface lattice and subunit structure and observations on reassembly, *J. Cell Biol.,* **60,** 153–67.

ESTENSEN, R. D., ROSENBERG, M. and SHERIDAN, J. E. (1971) Cytochalasin B: microfilaments and 'contractile' processes, *Science,* **173,** 356–9.

FAWCETT, D. W. and PORTER, K. R. (1954) A study of the fine structure of ciliated epithelia, *J. Morph.,* **94,** 221–81.

FORER, A. and BLECHER, S. R. (1975) Appearances of microtubules after various fixative procedures, and comparison with the appearances of tobacco mosaic virus, *J. Cell Sci.,* **19,** 579–605.

FORER, A., EMMERSEN, J. and BEHNKE, O. (1972) Cytochalasin B: does it affect actin-like filaments? *Science,* **175,** 774–6.

FUJIWARA, K. and POLLARD, T. D. (1976) Fluorescent antibody localization of myosin in the cytoplasm, cleavage furrow and mitotic spindle of human cells, *J. Cell Biol.,* **71,** 848–75.

FUJIWARA, K. and TILNEY, L. G. (1975) Substructural analysis of the microtubule and its polymorphic forms, *Ann. N.Y. Acad. Sci.,* **253,** 27–50.

FULTON, C. and KOWIT, J. D. (1975) Programmed synthesis of flagellar tubulin during cell differentiation in *Naegleria, Ann. N.Y. Acad. Sci.* **253,** 318–32.

GRIMSTONE, A. V. and KLUG, A. (1966) Observations on the substructure of flagella fibres, *J. Cell Sci.,* **1,** 351–62.

HARTWIG, J. H. and STOSSEL, T. P. (1976) Interactions of actin, myosin and an actin-binding protein of rabbit pulmonary macrophages. III. Effects of cytochalasin B, *J. Cell Biol.,* **71,** 295–303.

HATANO, S. and OOSAWA, F. (1966) Extraction of an actin-like protein from the plasmodium of a myxomycete and its interaction with myosin A from rabbit striated muscle, *J. Cell Physiol.,* **68**, 197–214.

HYAMS, J. S. and BORISY, G. G. (1978) Nucleation of microtubules *in vitro* by isolated spindle pole bodies of the yeast *Saccharomyces cerevrisiae., J. Cell Biol.,* **78**, 401–14.

INOUÉ, S. and SATO, H. (1967) Cell motility by labile association of molecules. The nature of mitotic spindle fibers and their role in chromosome movement, *J. Gen. Physiol.,* **50**, 259–92.

ISHIKAWA, H., BISCHOFF, R. and HOLTZER, H. (1969) Formation of arrowhead complexes with heavy meromyosin in a variety of cell types,*J. Cell Biol.,* **43**, 312–28.

KANE, R. G. (1974) Preparation and purification of polymerised actin from sea urchin egg extracts, *J. Cell Biol.,* **66**, 305–15.

KANE, R. G. (1976) Actin polymerization and interaction with other proteins in temperature-induced gelation of sea urchin egg extracts, *J. Cell Biol.,* **71**, 704–14.

LAZARIDES, E. and WEBER, K. (1974) Actin antibody: the specific visualisation of actin filaments in non-muscle cells, *Proc. Natl. Acad. Sci. USA,* **71**, 2268–72.

LEDBETTER, M. C. and PORTER, K. R. (1963) A 'microtubule' in plant cell fine structure, *J. Cell Biol.,* **19**, 239–50.

LEDBETTER, M. C. and PORTER, K. R. (1964) Morphology of microtubules of plant cells, *Science,* **144**, 872–4.

LOEWY, A. G. (1952) An actomyosin-like substance from the plasmodium of a myxomycete. *J. Cell Comp. Physiol.,* **40**, 127–56.

LUDUENA, R. F. and WOODWARD, D. O. (1973) Isolation and partial characterization of α and β tubulin from outer doublets of sea-urchin sperm and microtubules of chick-embryo brain, *Proc. Natl. Acad. Sci. USA,* **70**, 3594–8.

LUFTIG, R. B., McMILLAN, P. N., WEATHERBEE, J. A. and WEIHING, R. R. (1977) Increased visualization of microtubules by an improved fixation procedure, *J. Histochem. Cytochem.,* **25**, 175–87.

MALAWISTA, S. E., SATO, H. and BENSCH, K. G. (1968) Vinblastine and griseofulvin reversibly disrupt the living mitotic spindle, *Science,* **160**, 770–2.

MANDELKOW, E., THOMAS, E. and COHEN, C. (1977) Microtubule structure at low resolution by X-ray diffraction, *Proc. Natl. Acad. Sci. USA,* **74**, 3370–4.

MANTON, I. and CLARKE, B. (1952) An electron microscope study of the spermatozoid of *Sphagnum. J. Exp. Bot.,* **3**, 265–75.

McINTOSH, J. R. (1974) Bridges between microtubules, *J. Cell Biol.,* **61**, 166–87.

MEZA, I., HUANG, B. and BRYAN, J. (1972) Chemical heterogeneity of protofilaments forming the outer doublets from sea urchin flagella. *Exp. Cell Res.,* **74**, 535–40.

MURPHY, D. B. and BORISY, G. G. (1975) Association of high molecular weight proteins with microtubules and their role in microtubule assembly *in vitro, Proc. Natl. Acad. Sci. USA,* **72**, 2696–700.

MURPHY, D. B. and TILNEY, L. G. (1974) The role of microtubules in the movement of pigment granules in teleost melanophores, *J. Cell Biol.,* **61**, 757–79.

PEASE, D. C. (1963) The ultrastructure of flagellar fibrils, *J. Cell Biol.,* **18**, 313–26.

POLLARD, T. D. (1975) Functional implications of the biochemical and structural properties of cytoplasmic contractile proteins, in *Molecules and Cell Movement.* eds. S. Inoué and R. E. Stephens. Raven Press, N.Y.

POLLARD, T. D. (1976) The role of actin in the temperature-dependent gelation and contraction of extracts of *Acanthamoeba, J. Cell Biol.,* **68**, 579–601.

SANGER, J. (1975) Changing patterns of actin localization during cell division, *Proc. Natl. Acad. Sci. USA,* **72**, 1913–16.

SHELANSKI, M. L. and TAYLOR, E. W. (1968) Properties of the protein subunit of central pair and outer doublet microtubules of sea urchin flagella, *J. Cell Biol.,* **38**, 304–15.

SLAUTTERBACK, D. B. (1963) Cytoplasmic microtubules,*J. Cell Biol.,* **18**, 367–88.

SPUDICH, J. A. and LIN, S. (1972) Cytochalasin B, its interaction with actin and myosin from muscle, *Proc. Natl. Acad. Sci. USA*, **69**, 442–6.

STEBBINGS, H. and BENNETT, C. E. (1976) The effect of colchicine on the sleeve element of microtubules, *Exp. Cell Res.*, **100**, 419–23.

STEBBINGS, H. and WILLISON, J. H. M. (1973) A study of freeze-etched and negatively stained microtubules from the ovaries of *Notonecta, Z. Zellforsch,* **138**, 387–96.

STECK, T. L. (1974) The organization of proteins in the human red blood cell membrane, *J. Cell Biol.*, **62**, 1–19.

TILNEY, L. G. (1975) The role of actin in non-muscle cell motility, in *Molecules and Cell Movement,* eds. S. Inoué and R. E. Stephens. Raven Press, N.Y.

TILNEY, L. G. (1976a) The polymerization of actin. II. How non-filamentous actin becomes non-randomly distributed in sperm – evidence for the association of this actin with membranes, *J. Cell Biol.*, **69**, 51–72.

TILNEY, L. G. (1976b) The polymerization of actin. III. Non-filamentous aggregates of actin and its associated proteins – a storage form of actin, *J. Cell Biol.*, **69**, 73–89.

TILNEY, L. G., BRYAN, J., BUSH, D. J., FUJIWARA, K., MOOSEKER, M. S., MURPHY, D. B. and SNYDER, D. H. (1973) Microtubules: Evidence for 13 protofilaments, *J. Cell Biol.*, **59**, 267–75.

TILNEY, L. G. and DETMERS, P. (1975) Actin in erythrocyte ghosts and its association with spectrin. Evidence for a non-filamentous form of these two molecules *in situ, J. Cell Biol.*, **66**, 508–20.

WARFIELD, R. K. N. and BOUCK, G. B. (1974) Microtubule–macrotubule transitions: intermediates after exposure to the mitotic inhibitor vinblastine, *Science,* **186**, 1219–21.

WEBER, K., POLLACK, R. and BIBRING, T. (1975) Antibody against tubulin: The specific visualization of cytoplasmic microtubules in tissue culture cells, *Proc. Natl. Acad. Sci. USA,* **72**, 459–63.

WEIHING, R. R. (1976) Cytochalasin B inhibits actin-related gelation of HeLa cell extracts, *J. Cell Biol.*, **71**, 303–7.

WEISENBERG, R. C. (1972a) Changes in the organization of tubulin during meiosis in the eggs of the surf clam, *Spissula solidissima, J. Cell Biol.*, **54**, 266–78.

WEISENBERG, R. C. (1972b) Microtubule formation *in vitro* in solutions containing low calcium ions, *Science,* **177**, 1104–5.

WEISENBERG, R. C., BORISY, G. G. and TAYLOR, E. W. (1968) The colchicine binding protein of mammalian brain and its relation to microtubules, *Biochemistry,* **7**, 4466–79.

WESSELS, N. K., SPOONER, B. S., ASH, J. F., BRADLEY, M. O., LUDUENA, M. A., TAYLOR, E. C., WRENN, J. T. and YAMADA, K. M. (1971) Microfilaments in cellular and developmental processes, *Science,* **171**, 135–43.

WILSON, L. (1975) Microtubules as drug receptors: pharmacological properties of microtubule protein, *Ann. N.Y. Acad. Sci.,* **253**, 213–31.

WILSON, L. and MEZA, I. (1973) The mechanism of action of colchicine. Colchicine binding properties of sea urchin sperm tail outer doublet tubulin, *J. Cell Biol.*, **58**, 709–19.

WITMAN, G. B., CARLSON, K. and ROSENBAUM, J. L. (1972) *Chylamydomonas* flagella. II. The distribution of tubulins 1 and 2 in the outer doublet microtubules, *J. Cell Biol.*, **54**, 540–55.

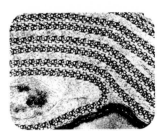

Chapter 3

Cilia, flagella, axostyles

In this chapter we shall consider examples of cell motility believed to be based entirely on microtubules. Cilia and flagella are motile cellular appendages which are found in widely divergent cell types throughout the plant and animal kingdoms. Since they project from the cell surface they can almost be thought of as 'extracellular' organelles, a fact which has greatly facilitated both the analysis of their movement and their isolation for biochemical and other studies. The contractile axostyle, on the other hand, is a truly intracellular structure found exclusively in a small group of parasitic protozoans. However, as we shall discover, the basis of their movement reveals sufficient similarities to warrant their consideration together. Since considerably more is known about cilia and flagella we shall discuss them first and in greatest detail.

3.1　The movement of cilia and flagella

Cilia and flagella perform one of two basic functions, either moving the cell through its environment or moving the environment relative to the cell. Both occasion the cilium or flagellum to move extremely rapidly, performing up to 60 beat cycles per second. Despite this, early microscopists were able to distinguish sufficiently distinct patterns of beating to coin separate names for the two organelles. The modern study of ciliary and flagellar movement began in the 1950s with the introduction of two new techniques. The first was the instantaneous fixation procedure of Parducz who showed that cilia and flagella 'frozen' in their beat cycle by chemical treatments were more easily analysed under the light microscope than the living organelle. The second was the use by Sir James Gray of a combination of dark-field microscopy and stroboscopic illumination to visualise the waveform of rapidly beating sea urchin spermatozoa. These techniques, together with cinematography and the examination of fixed material in the scanning electron microscope, remain our most effective tools for the analysis of ciliary and flagellar movement.

With the application of these new methods to a number of different organisms it became clear that a considerable variation existed in the pattern of ciliary and flagellar beating to the extent that intermediate forms, difficult to ascribe to either class, were identified. For the sake of simplicity we will consider here only the movement of 'typical' cilia and flagella although some idea of the variation which exists may be found in the review of Sleigh (1969).

The most extensively studied example of flagellar movement is that of the spermatozoa of various species of sea urchin. These organisms are easily maintained in the laboratory and may be repeatedly induced to shed sperm in vast numbers. Equally important, normal motility occurs outside the organism, in this case in sea water. This is not so for many animal sperm which may exhibit normal patterns of movement only in the female genital tract. Examination of this latter type involves the synthesis of artificial media which may correspond to conditions *in vivo* but which may also introduce unknown artefacts. The sea urchin spermatozoan consists of a conical-shaped head and a long (approximately 40 μm) slender flagellar tail. Bending waves pass distally along the flagellum at a constant amplitude and at a rate of approximately 9 μm s^{-1}. The waves have been described as consisting of straight regions alternating between circular arcs (Fig. 3.1). The bending of the flagellum is predominantly in one plane and is asymmetric about the long axis of the sperm, the degree of curvature in one direction, the *principal bend*, being greater than in the other, the *reverse bend*.

The movement of cilia is not as easily studied as that of flagella. Cilia tend to be shorter (5–15 μm) and are often densely packed on the surface of the cell or tissue. The typical ciliary beat is biphasic consisting of a rapid *effective stroke* in which the cilium is held rigid and bends only at its base, and a slow *recovery stroke* in which a wave passes from the base to the tip as the cilium returns to its original position (Fig. 3.1). The most significant difference in the movement associated with the two types of organelle is that force is directed along the axis of a flagellum but perpendicular to the axis of a cilium. For this reason flagellar movement is particularly associated with the propulsion of a cell such as a spermatozoan through its environment while cilia are particularly effective at moving fluid parallel to the cell surface, as is the case in various ciliated epithelia. Exceptions to such a broad

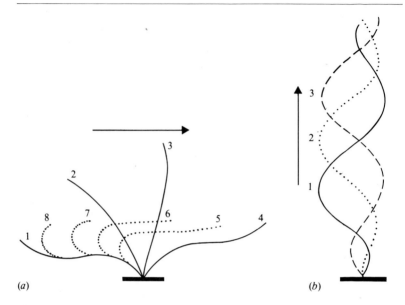

(a)   (b)

Fig. 3.1 Comparison of the wave forms generated by (*a*) cilia and (*b*) flagella. Stages through the effective and recovery strokes of the ciliary beat are shown by the solid and dotted lines respectively. Three stages in the propagation of an undulatory wave towards the distal tip of the flagellum are also indicated. The arrows denote the direction of the propulsion of water by the beating of the two organelles. (After M. A. Sleigh (1974).)

generalisation are immediately provided by certain protozoa, such as *Paramecium* and *Tetrahymena,* which are propelled efficiently by ciliary action.

One conspicuous feature of the motion of groups of cilia arranged in two dimensions is the coordination of their beating to form *metachronal waves* (Fig. 3.2). The beat of each cilium along the plane of the metachronal wave is precisely synchronised with each of its neighbours although each successive row beats out of phase in a precise sequence. Valentine in the 1840s likened this effect to waves passing across a cornfield stirred by the breeze. The basis of

Fig. 3.2 Coordination of ciliary motion to form metachronal waves as seen in the scanning electron microscope. (*a*) from the protozoan, *Opalina ranarum*; (*b*) from the digestive epithelium of a polychaete worm, *Cirriformia tentaculata*. The direction of wave transmission is from right to left in both cases. ((*a*) From G. A. Horridge and S. L. Tamm, *Science,* **163,** 817 (1969) courtesy of Dr S. L. Tamm. Copyright 1969 by the American Association for the Advancement of Science; (*b*) is from J. S. Mellor and J. S. Hyams (1978).

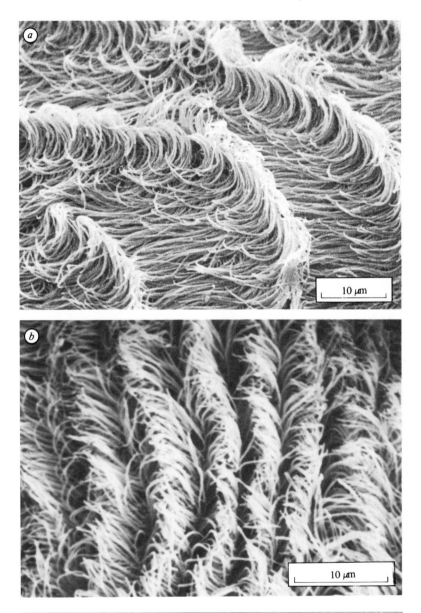

metachrony has occupied biologists for more than a century, during which time two theories have dominated. The 'neuroidal' theory envisaged that an internal excitation mechanism induced each cilium

71

to beat in a prescribed sequence while the 'mechanical' theory stated that ciliary coordination arose as the result of viscoelastic coupling between independent oscillators. With improvements in our techniques for measuring the hydrodynamic properties of ciliary movement the mechanical theory of ciliary coordination has become generally accepted (Machemer, 1974) although Tamm (1973) has shown that certain ctenophores may provide an exception to the rule.

3.1.1 Movement and behaviour

In organisms which are propelled through the medium by cilia or flagella, the latter serve not only as a motor but also as a rudder by which the cell can alter its direction of movement in response to external stimuli. Such movements are known as tactic or behavioural responses and they imply that the characteristic patterns of ciliary and flagellar beating described above are not inflexible but may vary so that the cell may be steered away from an unfavourable environment or towards a favourable one.

The involvement of cilia and flagella in the behaviour of certain ciliates and flagellates was first systematically investigated by Jennings in the early 1900s who found that the cilia of *Paramecium* responded to a variety of stimuli by reversing their direction of beating. With the application of electrophysiology to the study of ciliary reversal, it was found that the direction of ciliary beating was correlated with the electrical activity of the surface membrane and showed an absolute requirement for calcium ions. The involvement of both the cell membrane and external calcium was unambiguously demonstrated by the use of 'models' of *Paramecium*, cells which had been demembranated by treatment with detergent but in which motility was maintained by the addition of ATP (see Section 3.4). In the absence of the cell membrane the motile apparatus of the cilia was directly exposed to its environment which could be modified as desired. In concentrations of calcium below 10^{-7} M the models swam forward in a manner indistinguishable from living cells. However, upon raising the calcium level above 10^{-6} M the cilia were observed to swing through 180° so that now the effective stroke was directed towards the anterior of the cell and the direction of movement was reversed (Naitoh and Kaneko, 1972; Fig. 3.3). The sequence of events of ciliary reversal may be summarised as follows: the contact of a *Paramecium* with an obstacle or other stimulus induces the depolarisation of the surface membrane which allows calcium into the cell. Calcium initiates ciliary reversal which carries the cell away from the stimulus and causes the potential of the membrane to return to its resting level. Calcium is pumped out of the cell and forward swimming is resumed.

This mechanism has been shown to apply to other organisms although the change induced in the pattern of ciliary or flagellar

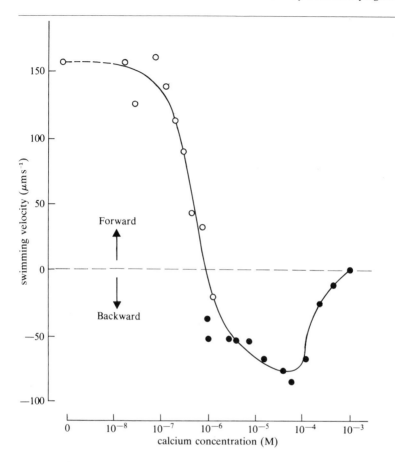

Fig. 3.3 The effect of Ca^{++} concentration on both swimming velocity and direction of movement in detergent extracted *Paramecium* reactivated in the presence of ATP. Swimming shows an abrupt transition from forwards to backwards as the concentration of calcium ions is raised above 10^{-6}M. (After Y. Naitoh and H. Kaneko (1972). Copyright 1972 by the American Association for the Advancement of Science.)

beating may vary. The flagellated trypanosome *Crithidia* generates typical bending waves which pass distally towards the tip of the flagellum until the cell encounters an obstacle, whereupon the waves proceed in the opposite direction and cause the cell to swim backwards. Such changes may be experimentally induced by the use of compounds called ionophores which specifically mediate the passage of calcium ions across the cell membrane (Holwill and McGregor, 1976).

In the biflagellate green alga, *Chlamydomonas reinhardtii,* a novel approach to the study of the behavioural responses of the cell has focused on the movement of the isolated flagellar apparatus. Pairs of flagella attached at their bases in a V configuration and detached from cells by gentle osmotic shock were found, upon the addition of ATP, to swim in a manner identical to the forward movement of living cells (Hyams and Borisy, 1978). When calcium was added to the environment, the beating of these isolated flagella changed markedly to now mimic the living cell during reverse motion. When the membranes were stripped from the isolated flagella by detergent treatment this alteration of waveform occurred at lower levels of calcium (10^{-7} M) than if the membranes were present (10^{-6} M), indicating that the membrane is involved in regulating the passage of ions into the flagellum. A reconstruction of the behaviour of *Chlamydomonas* based on the observation of these isolated pairs of flagella is shown in Fig. 3.4. Calcium must interact with specific acceptors within the flagellum but their identity and role in determining the pattern of ciliary or flagellar beating remains to be shown.

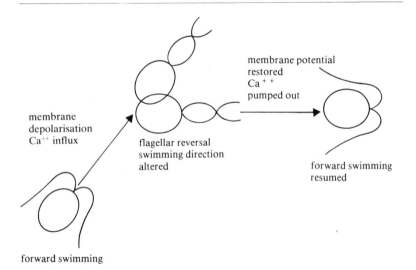

Fig. 3.4 Schematic representation of behavioural responses of the green alga, *Chlamydomonas*, induced by calcium ions. Various chemical or physical agents may stimulate the cell membrane, causing its depolarisation and allowing calcium to enter the cell. Binding of Ca^{++} to an unknown acceptor within the flagellum causes a change in the flagellar waveform and allows the cell to reorient with respect to the stimulus. Once out of contact with the inducer of the response, the electrical activity of the membrane returns to its resting level, calcium is pumped out of the cell and forward swimming is resumed. (From J. S. Hyams and G. G. Borisy, *J. Cell Sci.,* in press.)

3.2   Structure of the axoneme

The movements of cilia and flagella are generated by a single functional unit, the *axoneme*. The axoneme consists of a cylinder of nine equally spaced *outer doublet* microtubules surrounding two single central microtubules, the *central pair*. This arrangement is maintained by a delicate series of linkages to give the classical 9 + 2 pattern (Fig. 3.5*a* and 3.6). The axoneme is anchored to the cell by its attachment to a *basal body* (Fig. 3.5*b*). The basal body lies beneath the cell surface and is composed of nine microtubule triplets, groups of three microtubules arranged in a cartwheel-like array around the circumference of the basal body. The outer doublet microtubules of the axoneme are continuous with the inner two microtubules of each triplet while the central pair microtubules arise from an amorphous region at the distal end of the basal body. In many cells a conspicuous system of striated fibres referred to as 'rootlets' appears to extend from the basal body into the cell. As their name implies, these structures are assumed to provide anchorage for the basal body, enabling it to resist the considerable torque generated by the movement of the flagellum.

The outer doublets of the axoneme each consist of a complete microtubule of 13 protofilaments, the *A tubule*, with a partial microtubule of 10 protofilaments, the *B tubule*, attached longitudinally to it, three of the protofilaments serving as a common *partition wall* between the two elements. Each doublet is skewed with respect to the circumference of the axoneme so that the A tubule lies closer to the centre than the B (Fig. 3.6).

Attached to the A tubule, diametrically opposed to its junction with the B subfibre, are two *arms* which extend towards the B tubule of the adjacent doublet. When viewed from the base of the axoneme to the tip the arms always point in a clockwise direction. They are spaced at intervals of 22.5–24 nm along the A tubule and each has a characteristic morphology, the outer arm being conspicuously hooked when seen in transverse section.

Two other periodic elements are also associated with the A tubule of the outer doublet. *Radial spokes*, approximately 36 nm in length, extend from the inner surface of the A tubule and connect via *radial spoke heads* to projections associated with the surface of the central pair microtubules. The spokes are arranged in a two-start, left-handed helix around the axoneme. Thin sections or negatively stained preparations of frayed cilia or flagella reveal that the spokes can appear either as pairs or triplets depending on the species examined, although in either case each group exhibits a periodicity of 88–96 nm. The outer doublets are also connected circumferentially by *nexin links* which join the A tubule of the outer doublet to either the A or B tubule of the adjacent doublet. The 96 nm periodicity of the nexin links is almost identical to that of the radial spokes.

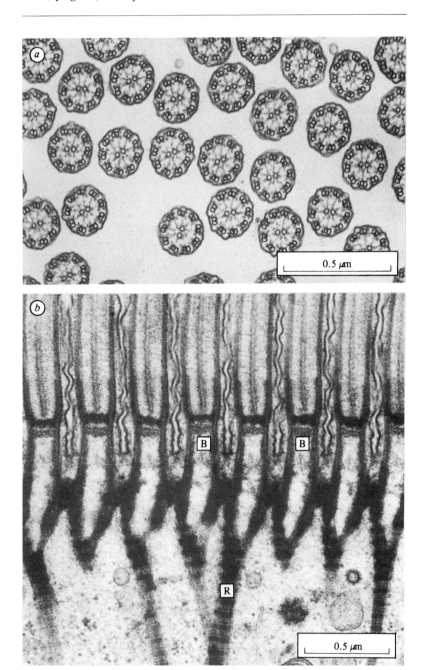

Fig. 3.5 Transverse (*a*) and longitudinal (*b*) sections of laterofrontal cilia from the freshwater lamellibranch, *Unio*. Most obvious in (*a*) are the 9 + 2 microtubules which are enclosed by the ciliary membrane. In (*b*) the complex series of striated rootlets (R) attached to the basal body (B) of each cilium are clearly seen. (Courtesy of Dr F. D. Warner.)

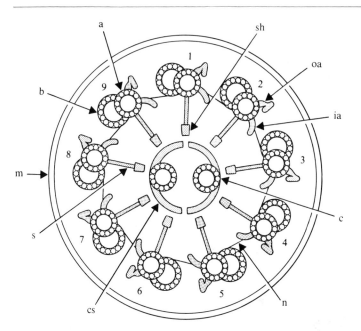

Fig. 3.6 Diagrammatic representation of a transverse section through a cilium or flagellum. (m) membrane, (a) and (b) A and B tubule of outer doublet, (oa) and (ia) outer and inner arm, (n) nexin link, (s) radial spoke, (sh) radial spoke head, (cs) projections from central pair, (c) central pair microtubule. (From H. Mohri, *Zoological Magazine* (Dobutsugaku Zasshi), **85**, 1–16 (1976).)

The central pair is always situated so that a line bisecting the two microtubules at right angles passes in one direction through one of the outer doublets (referred to as doublet no. 1) and in the other between two adjacent doublets (numbers 5 and 6). The conservation of this arrangement is probably explained by the finding of a number of authors that the plane of the ciliary or flagellar beat is perpendicular to the orientation of the central pair. The central pair was originally thought to be surrounded by a sheath of material to which the radial spoke heads attached. With improvements in electron microscope techniques and resolution this material has now been identified as two rows of projections located with a periodicity of 14–16 nm along the outer surface of each microtubule and arcing back towards the centre of the axoneme. The central pair projections subtend an angle of approximately 15° to the microtubule, those on the central microtubule nearest outer doublet number 8 pointing distally while those nearest doublet number 3 point towards the proximal end of the flagellum.

Can the structure of the flagellum tell us anything of how the movement of cilia and flagella is generated? Serial cross-sections through the gill cilia of the mollusc, *Elliptio*, fixed in known positions of the beat cycle, revealed that the relationship of the outer doublets altered systematically through the effective and recovery strokes (Satir, 1968). This was particularly obvious at the ciliary tip where the central pair microtubules extended beyond the outer doublets. Sections through the tip revealed, however, that the doublets on the inside of the bend extended further than those on the outside, indicating that there had been a displacement between them. Since the length of the microtubules had remained constant, the doublets on the inside of the bend could be said to have 'slid' relative to those on the outside. In analogy to the situation in striated muscle, this concept became known as the *sliding microtubule model of ciliary or flagellar movement* and is shown diagrammatically in Fig. 3.7.

An equally painstaking analysis of longitudinal sections through *Elliptio* gill cilia revealed that microtubule sliding was accompanied by changes in the position of the radial spokes (Warner and Satir, 1974). Each triplet of spokes exhibited a periodicity of 86 nm or a precise 6:1 relationship with the 14.3 nm repeat of the central pair projections. In straight regions the spokes appeared perpendicular to the outer doublet although the third member of the group frequently appeared tilted back towards the other two. In this latter configuration each spoke was directly aligned with, but not attached to, projections of the central pair. At the leading edge of a bend the spokes and central pair complex became firmly attached, microtubule sliding resulting in the distortion of the radial spokes which become tilted up to 33° from the perpendicular. At the trailing edge of the bend the spokes detach and the straight axonemal configuration is resumed. Thus it appears that the spokes and central pair complex undergo a precise cycle of attachment and detachment and it is this which restricts the amount of sliding between adjacent doublets leading to the formation of bends. More direct evidence to this point and to other features of the sliding microtubule model will be considered later in the chapter.

3.2.1 Variants of axonemal structure

Although the 9 + 2 is by far the most common axonemal configuration, variations in this pattern have been noted and will be considered briefly. Almost all of the differences occur in spermatozoa

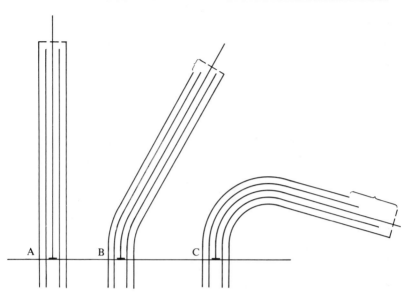

Fig. 3.7 Diagram illustrating the sliding of microtubules during ciliary bending. The shorter lines represent the outer doublet microtubules, the longer middle line the central pair. In the bent position (B, C), the doublets on the inside of the bend extend further than those on the outside. Since there has been no change in the length of the microtubules it can be envisaged that they have 'slid' over one another. The degree of sliding between the doublets on the inside and outside of the bend is indicated by the bracket. (After M. A. Sleigh, *Handbook of Molecular Cytology*, A. Lima-de-Faria, editor (1969).)

and many of them are to be found in the insects. The most frequent divergence from the basic $9 + 2$ is the addition of a ring of extra single microtubules peripheral to the outer doublets (the $9 + 9 + 2$ pattern, Fig. 3.8*a*). These *accessory tubules* often contain a dense central dot and exhibit conspicuous projections similar to the arms of the outer doublets. The other distinctive feature of insect sperm is the presence of one or more large, paracrystalline mitochondrial derivatives which extend almost the whole length of the flagellum and occupy most of the volume of the sperm tail. These flagella are among the longest known, the sperm of *Notonecta glauca* shown in Fig. 3.8*a* measuring up to 1.5 cm in length!

Other insect spermatozoa, and also those of certain polychaete worms, reveal variations in the central elements of the axoneme. These take the form of the substitution of the central pair by either an opaque core ($9 + 0$) or by 1, 3, 5 or 7 microtubules (the $9 + 1_n$ axoneme). These findings imply that the central pair is not essential for flagellar

79

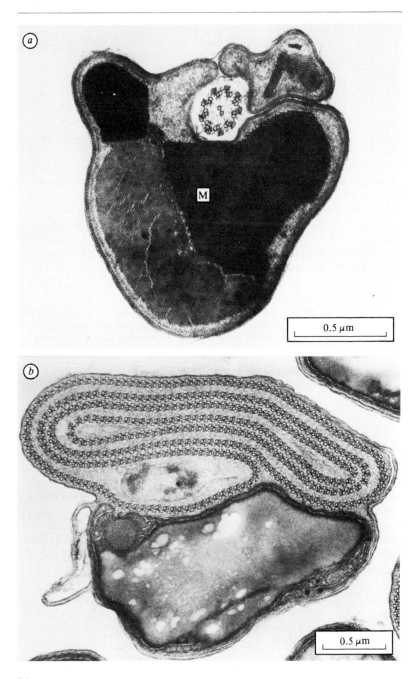

Fig. 3.8 Transverse sections through insect sperm (*a*) *Notonecta*. An outer ring of single microtubules surrounds the 9 + 2 axoneme. The large distinctive crystalline bodies are mitochondrial derivatives (M). (*b*) *Rhynchosciara*. The axoneme consists of over 300 doublet and single microtubules in an elaborate arrangement.

movement. The observation of insect sperm is complicated by the fact that they are normally motile only in the female tract. Despite this, movement of sperm with 9 + 9 + 2, 9 + 0 and 9 + 1_n axonemes has been observed. Particularly interesting in this regard is the finding that mutants of *Chlamydomonas* in which the central pair is disorganised, are non-motile (Randall, 1969). It would be extremely valuable to have more detailed observations on the beating of these variant flagella in order to correlate changes in the waveform with the structure of the axoneme.

Perhaps the most bizarre example of aberrant flagellar structure, however, is shown by the spermatozoa of *Rhynchosciara* (Fig. 3.8*b*). In this insect the flagellum is composed of over 300 doublet microtubules arranged in a spiral configuration which changes during spermiogenesis and fertilisation. Very few observations of these sperm have been made although it is known that they are motile.

3.3   Biochemistry of the axoneme

If one wishes to understand how a machine works it is a great advantage to possess a catalogue listing all of its components. This philosophy has been the impetus behind much of the considerable effort which has gone into attempts to characterise the components of the axoneme. Cilia and flagella are particularly well suited to this type of approach since:

1.   They are autonomous organelles containing all the machinery required to generate their own movement.
2.   They can be isolated in vast numbers for biochemical analysis.

The source of cilia and flagella for biochemical investigation has varied greatly. The most common early sources were the ciliated protozoan *Tetrahymena* and various unicellular green algae, both having the advantage of being easily grown in laboratory culture. More recently, the gills of certain molluscs and the sperm of some species of sea urchin have become increasingly favoured, especially by those workers fortunate enough to have a laboratory situated close to the ocean! The isolation of cilia usually follows a fairly common procedure regardless of source. Ciliated cells are subjected to some kind of osmotic, pH or mechanical trauma which results in the detachment of the cilia at their transition zones, that is the point at which the triplet

microtubules of the basal body become the doublets of the axoneme.
The basal body is apparently unaffected by this event since if the
deciliation treatment is sufficiently mild, new cilia will rapidly
regenerate. A brief centrifugation at about $1,000 \times g$ removes the cell
bodies and any large debris leaving the detached cilia in the
supernatant to be harvested by a longer spin in the region of
$10,000 \times g$.

Despite the simplicity of this procedure, fractionation of isolated
cilia and flagella was hindered for several years by their extreme
insolubility under all but the strongest denaturing conditions. This
dilemma was resolved by Gibbons (1963) who showed that the
impervious nature of isolated cilia was due to the presence of the
surrounding membrane. Removal of the membrane with digitonin
exposed the naked axoneme which could then be separated into its
enzymic and structural components which we shall now consider.

3.3.1 Dynein

The sliding microtubule model of ciliary and flagellar movement
predicts that the displacement between adjacent outer doublets is
effected by the mechanical action of cross-bridges extending between
them, using energy derived from the hydrolysis of ATP. Since the only
structures connecting the outer doublets circumferentially are the
arms and nexin links (Fig. 3.6), either or both of these elements are
therefore obvious candidates for the force-generating components of
the axoneme. Axonemes isolated from *Tetrahymena* by the digitonin
procedure revealed considerable ATPase activity. Dialysis against
tris-EDTA resulted in the extraction of the enzyme with the
concomitant disappearance of the arms attached to the A tubule of the
outer doublet, the nexin links however remained in their original
position.

The isolated ATPase was resolved in the analytical ultracentrifuge
into two components with sedimentation coefficients of $14S$ and $30S$.
In the presence of magnesium the $30S$ component rebounds to the
dialysed axonemes with the restoration of 60% of the original ATPase
activity. In the electron microscope it could be seen that reassociation
of the $30S$ component was accompanied by a return of the arms to their
original position on the A tubule (Gibbons, 1963, 1965). This was the
first direct demonstration that at least some of the axonemal ATPase
was associated with the arms although the location of the $14S$
component remained unknown.

With the development of a simple procedure for its purification, the
properties of axonemal ATPase were extensively examined. The $14S$
component was shown by electron microscopy to be an elipsoidal
molecule with a long diameter of approximately 14 nm. Since the $30S$
species appeared as a linear aggregate of similar sized globular units,

14S and 30S were thought to represent the monomeric and polymeric forms of a single protein which was named *dynein* (= force protein; Gibbons and Rowe, 1965). Both the 14S and 30S forms of dynein were shown to be extremely specific for ATP as a substrate and activation of the enzyme showed an absolute requirement for the presence of a divalent cation, particularly magnesium.

On SDS–polyacrylamide gels, axonemes and partially purified dynein revealed two bands with apparent molecular weights of 500,000 and 450,000 daltons. The designation A and B was applied to the larger and smaller polypeptides respectively. Extraction of flagellar axonemes with 0.5 M KCl resulted in the loss of half the A component (A1) together with 60–65% of the ATPase activity. The only structure removed by this procedure was the outer of the two arms, indicating quite convincingly that the A1 component constitutes the latter structure. Dialysis of ciliary axonemes revealed a somewhat different extraction of dynein, the B component being removed together with half the A, again presumably A1. Since 40–50% of the ATPase activity remained bound to the axoneme this suggested that the inner arm was composed of the less easily extracted A band component (A2) although it was not possible to confirm this point by electron microscopy. If correct, however, this supposition also implied that no ATPase activity was associated with the B band whose origin remained unknown.

Recently, a more rigorous characterisation of dynein has been attempted with the result that the situation now appears even more complex than before. Improved methods of SDS–gel electrophoresis have shown that dynein may be resolved into four components and not two as previously supposed. The newly designated C band exhibited a slightly higher molecular weight than the A component while D migrated between A and B. Fortunately, with this improved resolution a more sophisticated scheme for the separation of the different components provided some clarification (Gibbons *et al.*, 1976). ATPase activity was found to be associated with the A, C and D components but not with B as had been inferred from previous experiments. The unambiguous characterisation of the other three species required each of them to be purified for analysis of their enzymatic activity. So far this has been possible only for A and D both of which revealed distinct, albeit similar, ATPase activity. The most convincing evidence that these are in fact different proteins was obtained using an antiserum prepared against a tryptic fragment of dynein (fragment A) which precipitated A band protein and completely inhibited its ATPase activity while having no effect on the D component. For this reason the ATPase protein seen as band A on gels has been renamed *dynein 1* while the ATPase of the D band is now referred to as *dynein 2*. Dynein 1 has already been equated with the outer doublet arms but as yet the location of dynein 2 is unknown. Limited cytochemical studies have suggested that ATPase activity may be associated with the radial spokes or spoke heads and such a location for dynein 2 cannot be excluded. Further evidence awaits the characterisation of some of the minor axonemal components, possibly making use of flagellum mutants in which these structures may be missing.

3.3.2 The 9 + 2 microtubules

Gibbons's original scheme for the isolation of dynein proved to be of even wider significance to the study of the biochemistry of other components of the axoneme. In solubilising the dynein arms and central pair this method left behind pure preparations of outer doublet microtubules (Fig. 3.9). The subsequent discovery that the A and B tubules could themselves be separated on the basis of their differential temperature stability provided a basis for the analysis of axonemal microtubule proteins. Preparations of doublets in 1 mM tris-HCl, pH 8.0 containing 0.1 mM GTP were warmed to 37°C and rapidly cooled to 0°. This treatment resulted in the solubilisation of the B tubule leaving the singlet A microtubules. The A tubules could in turn be dissolved in 0.5% sarkosyl to yield a $3S$ monomer which, upon tenfold dilution of the detergent, reassociated into a mixture of singlet microtubules and protofilaments. Soluble B tubulin existed mainly as a $6S$ dimer which upon addition of 0.05 M NaCl and 1 mM MgCl$_2$ reassembled into a mixture of ribbons of up to 10 protofilaments in width and sheets of broader dimension. Thus the tubulin from both the A and B tubule reassociated to resemble the structure from which it was derived, a singlet microtubule in the case of the A and a non-closed sheet of protofilaments for the B (Stephens, 1975). The logical question to then ask was whether, if one added preformed A tubules to solutions of tubulin derived from the B tubule, the mixture would assemble into doublets. In fact the B-derived tubulin formed only ribbons and sheets of protofilaments as it had done in the absence of A microtubules, suggesting that the formation of the complete doublet may require the presence of a templet. The basal body provides such a function during the *in vivo* assembly of the flagellar microtubules.

The observed differences in the stability of A and B tubules and the association properties of their tubulin could indicate that each is assembled from a chemically distinct molecule. The α and β chains of tubulin derived from both the A and B tubule were separated by preparative polyacrylamide gel electrophoresis, exploiting the fact that in alkaline conditions and in the presence of SDS the α chain

Fig. 3.9 Schematic representation of the biochemical fractionation of the axoneme. (After R. E. Stephens in *Cilia and Flagella*, M. A. Sleigh editor, Academic Press (1972).)

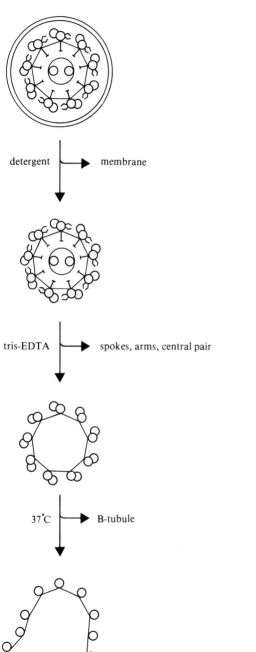

detergent → membrane

tris-EDTA → spokes, arms, central pair

37°C → B-tubule

migrates slower than the β. Amino acid analysis of each fraction showed that the α and β tubulin subunits derived from the A microtubules (αA βB) were significantly different from their counterparts in the B tubule (αB βB). The intriguing possibility that the central pair and cytoplasmic microtubules are composed of yet different tubulin molecules, each demonstrating characteristic and unique stability in response to both temperature and proteolysis, awaits more extensive comparative amino acid data. Until this is available the observed differences in stability could be ascribed to the interaction of the microtubules with other proteins.

3.3.3 Minor proteins

Axonemes subjected to SDS–polyacrylamide gel electrophoresis reveal, in addition to tubulin and dynein, some 30 additional bands, although the greater resolution of two-dimensional separation puts this figure at over 100. These proteins are collectively referred to as minor proteins, a term which describes only the small relative contribution each makes to the total axonemal protein and does not assess their importance to motility. Since these proteins are present in such small quantities they are much more difficult to characterise than the proteins of the arms and outer doublet microtubules but fortunately some scientists are stimulated by such a challenge and their findings will be discussed.

In axonemes which have been dialysed to remove the arms and central pair and thermally fractionated to remove the B tubule, A tubules are frequently seen to retain their cylindrical organisation due to persisting circumferential linkages. Solubilisation of the A tubules by treatment at pH 3 left a protein with molecular weight of 165,000 daltons and which constituted some 2% of the total axonemal protein. This protein was termed *nexin* (= binding protein).

The location of other minor bands has been determined by different procedures of axonemal fractionation. At least 10 minor bands, constituting 20–30% of the total protein, appear in preparations of outer doublet microtubules. None of these is released by thermal fractionation indicating that they are associated with the A tubule. Treatment of the A tubule with 0.5% sarkosyl, 0.3 M KSCN or 0.6 M KCl digests most of the microtubule wall but leaves a stable ribbon of three protofilaments to which four of the minor bands remain attached (Linck, 1976). As yet no role has been suggested for these protein species either in the assembly of the axoneme, the binding of other axonemal components to the A tubule, or motility.

A different and very exciting approach to the identification of the minor components of the axoneme has been the analysis of the paralysed flagellum mutants of *Chlamydomonas reinhardtii*. Comparison of mutants pf-15A and pf-19, in which the two central tubules are replaced with a core of disorganised material, with wild type revealed that two bands of molecular weight in excess of 220,000 daltons were either absent, or present in extremely reduced levels. Although it remains to be shown conclusively, these proteins could have derived from the central pair projections. More convincing were gels of another mutant, pf-14, which lacks radial spokes and revealed a band of molecular weight 116,000 daltons at only 30–40% of the wild type levels (Witman *et al.*, 1976). That this band is not absent altogether may be due to the fact that many of these paralysed flagellum mutants are 'leaky', i.e. in any culture a proportion of the cells will express the wild type phenotype, in this case produce radial spokes.

A more sophisticated approach to the identification of the radial spoke protein in pf-14 involved labelling the minor flagellar proteins of *C. reinhardtii* to very high specific activity by growing the cells in medium containing ^{35}S. Separation of the wild type axonemal proteins in one direction by isoelectric focusing and in a second by gel electrophoresis in the presence of SDS allowed over 100 peptides to be resolved by autoradiography. Gels of pf-14 axonemes revealed that 12 of these proteins were absent, while in yet another mutant, pf-1, which lacks only the radial spoke heads, only 6 of the 12 were missing. Clearly these mutants will be invaluable in identifying the minor components of the axoneme. When separation is efficient enough to allow antibodies to be made against the various minor elements and assayed for their effect on ciliary and flagellar movement *in vitro*, the role of these structures in motility will be more clearly understood.

3.4   Reactivation

The concept that cilia and flagella could be induced to resume normal motility, i.e. be *reactivated*, when detached from the cell, was pioneered by Hoffman-Berling who showed that flagella isolated by glycerination would resume normal bending movements when supplied with ATP. The great attraction of this kind of approach is that it permits the experimental manipulation of the motile apparatus of the flagellum in any way suggested by the experimenters' imagination. Early work was hampered by an inability to achieve preparations, in which more than 25–50% of the isolated flagella were motile. It quickly became clear that the barrier to the efficient analysis of motility *in vitro* was the presence of the flagellar membrane which prevented ATP from reaching the axoneme.

This problem was overcome by Gibbons and Gibbons (1972) who found that sea urchin sperm treated with a buffered 0.04% solution of the non-ionic detergent Triton X-100, were completely demembranated and would reactivate in the presence of 1 mM ATP with virtually 100% efficiency. These sperm performed on average 32 beats per second and moved at a rate of 90 μm s^{-1}, figures which are almost identical to the values recorded for live sperm in sea water which achieved 46 beats per second and moved at 160 μm s^{-1}. The waveform of the reactivated sperm also closely resembled that seen *in vivo* (Fig. 3.10). The reactivated sperm exhibited an ATPase activity which was tightly coupled to their movement, being four times greater in motile sperm than in those which had been immobilised by homogenisation. Most interesting, however, was the observation that conditions which favoured optimal motility, the presence of a divalent cation notably magnesium and the specificity for ATP, were virtually identical to those favouring the activation of isolated dynein (Section 3.3.1).

Demembranated sperm which prior to reactivation had been extracted with 0.5 M KC1, a treatment which removes half of the axonemal dynein 1 together with the outer of the two arms (Section 3.3.1), exhibited a beat frequency half that of the unextracted controls although the nature of the bending waves was unchanged (Gibbons and Gibbons, 1973). More gentle extraction revealed a direct correspondence between the decrease in beat frequency and the disappearance of the arms. Addition of soluble dynein 1 resulted in a gradual increase in beat frequency which was eventually restored to approximately 80% of its original value. These results demonstrate that beat frequency depends directly upon the number of arms present and also that the two arms are functionally identical, each contributing equally to the movement of the sperm.

A major contribution to our understanding of the mechanism of flagellar movement was provided by the experiments of Summers and Gibbons (1973) who subjected axonemes to gentle treatment with trypsin. When examined by dark-field light microscopy these axonemes appeared normal morphologically but upon the addition of ATP were seen to disintegrate rapidly into their component outer doublets. Axonemes were seen either to extend up to seven or eight times their original length, with a corresponding decrease in diameter, or else to extrude groups of microtubules from their distal ends. These observations were interpreted as suggesting that the doublets could slide over one another, the seven to eightfold increase in length

---

Fig. 3.10 Dark-field light micrographs of spermatozoa from the sea urchin, *Colobocentrotus*. (*a*) live sperm swimming in sea water, (*b*) detergent extracted sperm swimming in a defined salt solution containing ATP. In both cases the micrographs are of a single sperm and have been arranged in series to illustrate the passage of a typical undulatory wave along the flagellar tail. (From B. H. Gibbons and I. R. Gibbons (1972).)

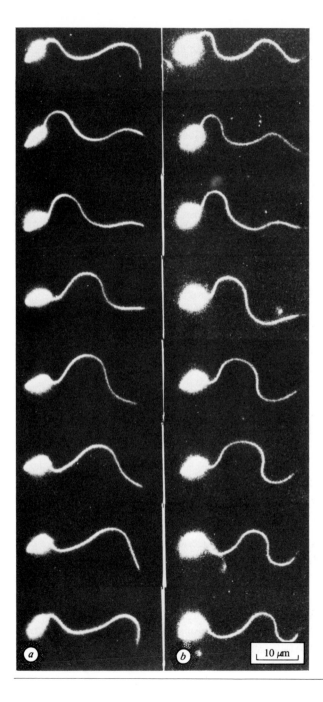

indicating that all of the doublets could participate (Fig. 3.11). That this sliding was in some way related to normal motility was shown by the finding that conditions favouring axonemal disintegration corresponded directly to those in which the optimal reactivation of untrypsinised axonemes occurred. In the electron microscope it could be seen that trypsin treatment resulted in the removal of the radial spokes and nexin linkages but that the dynein arms were not affected. These results demonstrate very convincingly that the movement of cilia and flagella is generated by sliding between adjacent doublets but that other components, radial spokes, nexin linkages, are required to convert this sliding into the typical bending movements of the flagellum.

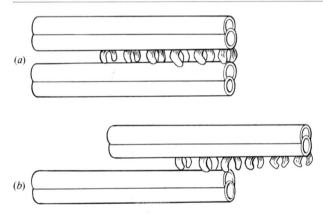

Fig. 3.11 Diagram depicting microtubule sliding. (*a*) illustrates a pair of adjacent doublet microtubules from a trypsin-treated axoneme. The radial spokes and nexin links have been digested by the enzyme but the dynein side arms still connect the doublets. Upon the addition of ATP (*b*) the upper doublet slides relative to the lower one as the dynein arms 'walk' along it. In an intact cilium or flagellum this dyneinmediated-sliding between adjacent doublets is constrained by the radial spokes and possibly also the nexin linkages to produce the characteristic bending movements. (From P. Satir, in *Cell Motility*, R. Goldman *et al.*, editors, pp. 841–6 (1976).)

Further evidence to support this conclusion was provided by the paralysed flagellum mutants of *Chlamydomonas reinhardtii* pf-14 and pf-15A which lack radial spokes and central pair microtubules respectively but which both possess morphologically normal dynein arms. Isolated axonemes from both mutants failed to reactivate but when trypsinised underwent rapid disintegration in the presence of ATP. These results again clearly demonstrate the participation of the spokes and central pair complex in the conversion of intradoublet sliding into bending.

To understand the generation of sliding during flagellar movement it is necessary to envisage the cyclic attachment and detachment of the arms of the A tubule with binding sites on the B tubule of the adjacent doublet using energy derived from the hydrolysis of ATP. In the vast majority of sections of flagella, however, the arms are seen to extend towards the B tubule but are rarely seen to form the transient cross-bridge predicted by the model. This problem was greatly clarified with the finding that a rapid fiftyfold dilution of ATP caused the movement of reactivated sperm to cease with them frozen into bent positions typical of the normal propagated wave of swimming sperm. By analogy with muscle (Chapter 1), these immobilised bends were termed 'rigor' waves. Digestion with trypsin caused no change in the rigor waves demonstrating that the dynein arms were principally responsible for their maintenance, a conclusion confirmed by electron microscopy which revealed that the arms were frequently seen to form cross-bridges between adjacent doublets.

3.5 Axostyles

Like the ciliary and flagellar axoneme, the axostyles of certain parasitic protozoa provide another example in which movement is generated by an ordered array of microtubules. The anaerobic flagellate *Saccinobacculus* inhabits the hindgut of the wood-eating roach, *Cryptocercus*. Extending the length of the cell is a ribbon-like bundle of singlet microtubules, the axostyle, along which successive bending waves pass in a posterior direction (Fig. 3.12). Unlike the situation in the axoneme, the microtubules of the axostyle are arranged not circumferentially but in parallel rows. Microtubules in a given row are connected by regular bridges, 16 nm long by 3 nm in diameter which exhibit a periodicity of 14–15 nm. Bridges also exist between microtubules in adjacent rows but are less regular (Fig. 3.13).

In an elegant analysis of bent and unbent regions of axostyles by electron microscopy, it was shown that sliding occurred between adjacent rows of microtubules (McIntosh *et al.*, 1973; McIntosh, 1973). The significance of these observations became clearer with the finding that axostyles could be isolated from cells under conditions which allowed their reactivation *in vitro* (Mooseker and Tilney, 1973). Just as with reactivated sperm, preparations of isolated axostyles could be obtained which exhibited 100% motility and performed movements characteristic of the organelle *in situ*. Most importantly, the conditions favouring the reactivation of the axostyle closely corresponded to those previously described for the motility of sea urchin sperm flagella, exhibiting a specificity for ATP and requiring the presence of magnesium. Polyacrylamide gels of isolated axostyles revealed many

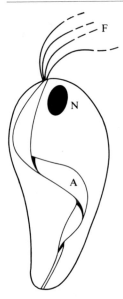

Fig. 3.12 Diagram to show the position of the axostyle within the flagellate *Saccinobacculus* (A) axostyle, (N) nucleus, (F) flagella. (After A. V. Grimstone and L. R. Cleveland, *J. Cell Biol.*, **24**, 387 (1965).)

proteins which corresponded to axonemal components but most notably a band which comigrated with dynein 1. Extraction of the isolated organelles with 0.5 M KC1 provided further evidence for the presence of dynein in the axostyle, this treatment resulting in the disorganisation of the parallel rows of microtubules due to the extraction of the intra-row bridges (Bloodgood, 1975). Extracted axostyles retained only one-third of the ATPase activity of unextracted controls.

Thus a large body of evidence suggests that the movement of the axostyle closely resembles that of cilia and flagella in that:

1. Force is generated by sliding between microtubules.
2. This force is generated by the ATPase protein dynein.
3. Sliding is converted into local bending by other structural components, the radial spokes and nexin linkages of cilia and flagella, and the inter-row bridges of the axostyle.

We have seen in this chapter two examples in which microtubules are clearly yet indirectly involved in movement by serving as a structural framework upon which mechanochemical, force-producing enzymes are organised. It is worth considering briefly whether such a

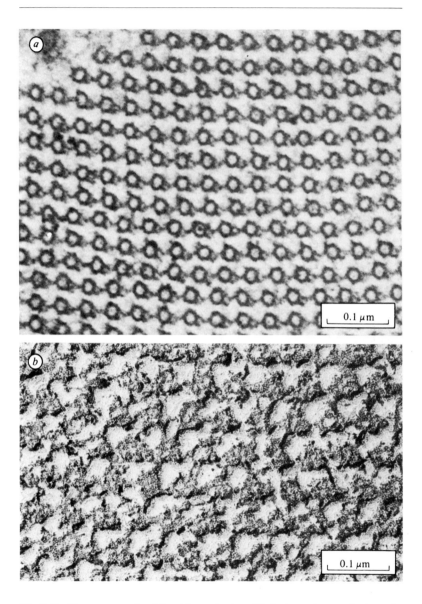

Fig. 3.13 Transverse section (*a*) and freeze fracture (*b*) electron micrographs through a portion of the axostyle of *Saccinobacculus*. In (*a*) in particular, bridges can be seen to extend between microtubules both in the same and adjacent rows. (Courtesy of Dr R. A. Bloodgood.)

sliding tubule mechanism of movement is unique to the examples quoted above or has a broader significance in cell motility. The answer to such a question is at present far from clear, notably because most other motile systems are not so readily amenable to either biochemical analysis or to reactivation *in vitro*. However, there is some evidence to suggest the presence of ATPase activity with the mitotic spindles of sea urchin eggs, and limited anaphase chromosome movements have been achieved in isolated mammalian spindles in the presence of ATP. This question became even more interesting with the demonstration that the mitotic apparatus, cortex and cleavage furrow of sea urchin eggs was decorated with fluorescent antibody produced against fragment A of axonemal dynein 1. Although a vast amount of work remains to be done the possibility that dynein-mediated microtubule sliding is an important feature of other motile phenomena cannot yet be discounted.

Suggestions for further reading and references

Further reading

SATIR, P. (1974) How cilia move, *Scientific American*, **231**, 4, 44–53.
SLEIGH, M. A. (1974) ed. *Cilia and Flagella*. Academic Press, N.Y.
SUMMERS, K. (1975) The role of flagellar structures in motility, *Biochimica et Biophysica Acta*, **416**, 153–68.

References

BLOODGOOD, R. A. (1975) Biochemical analysis of axostyle motility, *Cytobios*, **14**, 101–20.
GIBBONS, B. H. and GIBBONS, I. R. (1972) Flagellar movement and adenosine triphosphatase activity in sea urchin sperm extracted with triton X-100, *J. Cell Biol.*, **54**, 75–97.
GIBBONS, B. H. and GIBBONS, I. R. (1973) The effect of partial extraction of dynein arms on the movement of reactivated sea-urchin sperm, *J. Cell Sci.*, **13**, 337–57.
GIBBONS, I. R. (1963) Studies on the protein components of cilia from *Tetrahymena pyriformis*, *Proc. Natl. Acad. Sci.*, **50**, 1002–10.
GIBBONS, I. R. (1965) Chemical dissection of cilia, *Arch. Biol. (Liege)*, **76**, 317–52.
GIBBONS, I. R., FRONK, E., GIBBONS, B. H. and OGAWA, K. (1976) Multiple forms of dynein in sea urchin sperm flagella, in *Cell Motility*, eds. R. Goldman, T. Pollard and J. Rosenbaum. Cold Spring Harbor Publications, N.Y.
GIBBONS, I. R. and ROWE, A. J. (1965) Dynein: a protein with adenosine triphosphatase activity from cilia, *Science*, **149**, 424–6.
HOLWILL, M. E. J. and McGREGOR, J. L. (1976) Effects of calcium on flagellar movement in the trypanosome *Crithidia oncopelti*, *J. Exp. Biol.*, **65**, 229–42.
HYAMS, J. S. and BORISY, G. G. (1978) Isolated flagellar apparatus of *Chlamydomonas*. Characterisation of forward swimming and alteration of waveform and reversal of motion by calcium ions *in vitro*, *J. Cell Sci.*, **33**, 235–53.
LINCK, R. W. (1976) Flagellar doublet microtubules: fractionation of minor components and α-tubulin from specific regions of the A-tubule, *J. Cell Sci.*, **20**, 405–39.

References

MACHEMER, H. (1974) Ciliary activity and metachronism in Protozoa, in *Cilia and Flagella,* ed. M. A. Sleigh. Academic Press, N.Y.

McINTOSH, J. R., OGATA, E. S. and LANDIS, S. C. (1973) The axostyle of *Saccinobacculus.* I. Structure of the organism and its microtubule bundle, *J. Cell Biol.,* **56,** 304–23.

McINTOSH, J. R. (1973) The axostyle of *Saccinobacculus.* II. Motion of the microtubule bundle and structural comparison of straight and bend axostyles, *J. Cell Biol.,* **56,** 324–39.

MOOSEKER, M. S. and TILNEY, L. G. (1973) Isolation and reactivation of the axostyle. Evidence for a dynein-like ATPase in the axostyle, *J. Cell Biol.,* **56,** 13–26.

NAITOH, Y. and KANEKO, H. (1972) Reactivated triton-extracted models of *Paramecium*: modification of ciliary movement by calcium ions, *Science,* **176,** 523–4.

RANDALL, Sir JOHN (1969) The flagellar apparatus as a model organelle for the study of growth and morphopoiesis, *Proc. Roy. Soc. B,* **173,** 31–62.

SATIR, P. (1968) Studies on cilia. III. Further studies on the cilium tip and a 'sliding filament' mode of ciliary motility, *J. Cell Biol.,* **39,** 77–94.

SLEIGH, M. A. (1969) Coordination of the rhythm of beat in some ciliary systems, *Int. Rev. Cytol.,* **25,** 31–54.

STEPHENS, R. E. (1975) Structural chemistry of the axoneme: evidence for chemically and functionally unique tubulin dimers in outer fibres, in *Molecules and Cell Movement,* eds S. Inoué and R. E. Stephens. Raven Press, N.Y.

SUMMERS, K. and GIBBONS, I. R. (1973) Effects of trypsin digestion on flagellar structures and their relationship to motility, *J. Cell Biol.,* **58,** 618–29.

TAMM, S. L. (1973) Mechanisms of ciliary coordination in Ctenophores, *J. Exp. Biol.,* **59,** 231–45.

WARNER, F. D. and SATIR, P. (1974) The structural basis of ciliary bend formation, *J. Cell Biol.,* **63,** 35–63.

WITMAN, G. B., FAY, R. and PLUMMER, J. (1976) *Chlamydomonas* mutants: evidence for the roles of specific axonemal components in flagellar movement, in *Cell Motility,* eds R. Goldman, T. Pollard and J. Rosenbaum. Cold Spring Harbor Publications, N.Y.

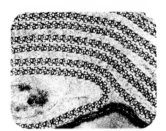

Chapter 4

Cell movements, microfilaments and contractile proteins

With the identification of actin and myosin in many eukaryotic cells (Chapter 2), the possibility of their involvement in a wide range of cell movements has received considerable attention. The comparability in properties between actin and myosin from muscle and non-muscle cells would seem to favour similarity in their motile mechanisms. In fact Huxley (1973) has advanced the argument that the actin filament/myosin head interaction might have been developed as a motile mechanism early in evolution and has since been highly conserved, reaching its greatest degree of organisation in striated muscle.

Although attractive, a universal mechanism should not be assumed before the location of actin and myosin within various non-muscle cells is clearly established, and factors which might regulate their action are identified. As can best be seen from the selected examples described in this chapter, the striking features which emerge are not only the marked variations which exist in both the arrangements of contractile proteins and the stability of the filaments they comprise, but also the apparent similarity in factors which control motility in many instances.

At one end of the scale, actin alone is involved in the acrosome reactions of certain sperm; by contrast, in the slime mould, *Physarum*, and in fresh water amoebae, transient actin and myosin filaments are involved in cytoplasmic streaming; still further, cells migrating in culture contain aligned filamentous actomyosin fibrils associated with structures which are analagous to the Z lines of striated muscle; and most ordered of all is the precise arrangement of actin and myosin filaments in the microvilli of intestinal epithelial cells, which resembles quite closely their arrangement in a muscle sarcomere.

4.1 Acrosome reactions

In many invertebrates, the problem of how the sperm is to penetrate the protective layers of the egg is overcome by the explosive discharge of a process from the anterior of the sperm head, known as the *acrosome*. Isolated sperm may be induced to undergo the acrosomal reaction spontaneously simply by exposing them to various abnormal ionic conditions, an observation which has allowed Tilney (1975a, 1976a, b) to identify two quite different mechanisms whereby microfilaments are involved in the generation of this remarkable form of motility.

Thyone   Within 10 seconds of activation, the sperm of the sea cucumber, *Thyone*, forms a process 0.5 μm in diameter and 90 μm in length. The acrosome is packed with microfilaments, 5 nm in diameter, which have been shown by the usual criteria to be composed of actin. Examination of unreactivated sperm showed that the periacrosomal material, from which the filaments of the process derived, was located in a cup-shaped indentation of the sperm nucleus and revealed an amorphous structure resembling a pellet of G-actin. High speed centrifugation of extracted sperm failed to sediment this material which was obviously non-filamentous and presumably in monomeric form (Section 2.4.3). Hence the explosive movement of the acrosomal discharge was achieved through the rapid polymerisation of actin filaments. Examination of the periacrosomal material by SDS–polyacrylamide gel electrophoresis revealed the presence of actin and two other proteins responsible for its maintenance in the depolymerised state, but no myosin.

Limulus   The acrosomal reaction of the sperm of the horseshoe crab, *Limulus*, was essentially similar to that of *Thyone* in that activation resulted in the rapid discharge of a process 50 μm in length and packed with microfilaments (Fig. 4.1*b* and *c*). Unlike the situation in echinoderm sperm, however, the filaments of the *Limulus* acrosomal process were already assembled prior to discharge, and stored in a coil around the base of the nucleus (Fig. 4.1*a*). In addition to this coiled configuration, the acrosome was also found to exist in two other states, the true discharge where the process was ejected from the anterior of the sperm head in response to calcium ions, and the false discharge where it projected posteriorly close to the sperm tail when the sperm was brought into contact with sea water. In both types of discharge, the process was seen to rotate so that the acrosome literally corkscrewed its way into the egg.

   A comparison of the structure of each state of the acrosomal process by electron microscopy showed that in the true discharge the microfilaments were aligned in parallel, with the periodicities of

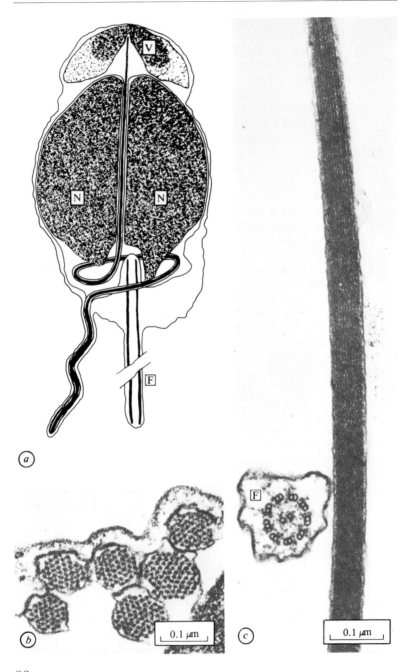

(a)

(b)   0.1 μm

(c)   0.1 μm

Fig. 4.1 The acrosomal reaction of *Limulus*. (*a*) Diagram showing the whole sperm, including the acrosomal vesicle (V), the nucleus (N) and the sperm flagellum (F). (*b*) Transverse section through the filament coils at the base of the sperm, showing the hexagonal packing of the microfilaments within each bundle. (*c*) Longitudinal section through an acrosomal process showing the aligned microfilaments. Also seen is a sperm flagellum (F). (From L. G. Tilney, (1975a).)

adjacent filaments in perfect register. In both the coiled configuration and the false discharge, on the other hand, filaments were seen to twist over one another although subtle differences were observed between the two. Since there was no overall change in the length of the acrosome before and after discharge, this amazing movement must have been brought about by alteration in the packing of the microfilaments. Isolation of the false discharge allowed an examination of the filament bundle by gel electrophoresis. This revealed the presence of three proteins, actin plus two others (not the same two as found in the acrosomes of *Thyone*), neither of which was myosin.

The acrosome reactions of both *Thyone* and *Limulus* represent quite remarkable examples of cell motility generated by actin in the complete absence of myosin. In one case this was achieved by the polymerisation of microfilaments, and in the other by an alteration of their lateral association. Tilney (1975b) believes that these observations may be of wider significance to other examples of non-muscle motility. While not denying that some of the movements of non-muscle cells will be shown to be based on actin–myosin interactions, other mechanisms based entirely on actin cannot be precluded. Several persuasive arguments are used to support this hypothesis. First, although actin is frequently the single most common cellular protein, myosin may be present in minute quantities or absent altogether. Second, unlike muscle, the microfilaments of non-muscle cells are often transitory, being formed and broken down continuously so that a mechanism which controls the polymerisation of actin must be basic to all cells. Third, it is naive to believe that just because a cell contains actin it must generate movement in the same way as one of the most highly specialised of all cells, striated muscle.

4.2 Shuttle streaming in slime moulds

Protoplasmic streaming within the plasmodia of slime moulds, and particularly *Physarum polycephalum*, has received a great deal of attention. This is due to the dramatic rate of streaming and the large volume of protoplasm transported, as well as to such practical considerations as its ease of culture and the ability to obtain large

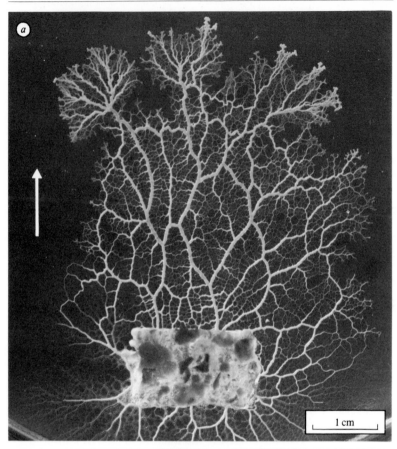

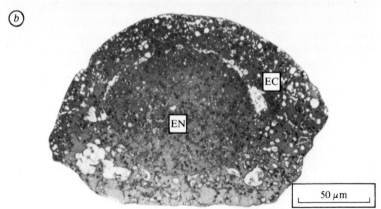

Fig. 4.2 *Physarum.* (*a*) A migrating plasmodium showing the network of plasmodial strands. The arrow denotes the direction of migration. (*b*) Transverse section through a plasmodial strand. The peripheral ectoplasm (EC) surrounds the inner endoplasm (EN).

quantities of material for biochemical studies. The plasmodia exist in the form of a network of protoplasmic strands of approximately 1 mm in diameter (Fig. 4.2*a*), each composed of an outer ectoplasmic tube of gel-like protoplasm around a sol-like endoplasm (Fig. 4.2*b*).

The endoplasm within the strands of *Physarum* streams at a rate approaching 1.3 mm s^{-1} and shows frequent reversal – hence the name *shuttle streaming*. Migration of the whole plasmodium occurs, therefore, when the net movement in one direction exceeds that in the opposite direction.

A seemingly unending number of hypotheses have been advanced to explain the mechanism of protoplasmic streaming, including forces due to surface tension, hydration, osmosis, sol–gel reversibility, myelin processes, caocervates, autonomous propulsion of particles, kinetic energy, magnetism, electrical forces, and contractility (see Seifriz, 1943). However, the situation became much clearer with the demonstration by Kamiya (1959) that the endoplasm streams passively along a pressure gradient. This was shown by means of the 'double-chamber method' in which a plasmodium was arranged within an apparatus (Fig. 4.3) in such a way that two plasmodial masses were

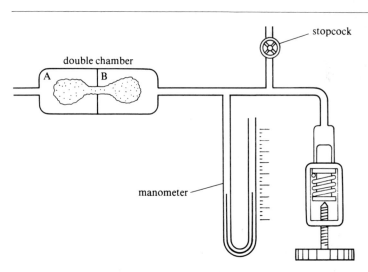

Fig. 4.3 Diagram showing the essential features of the apparatus used for measuring the motive force of protoplasmic streaming in a myxomycete plasmodium. The plasmodium is placed in either half of a double chamber (A and B), connected by a single plasmodial strand. (Redrawn from N. Kamiya, (1959).)

in separate but adjacent chambers joined by a single plasmodial strand. The motive force could then be determined from the counter pressure necessary to just prevent endoplasmic streaming.

Such findings were quickly followed by the proposal that the hydraulic pressure is generated by protoplasmic contractions. Accordingly, contraction of the ectoplasm at one end of a strand would create a pressure and so propel the endoplasm to the other end, with shuttle streaming resulting from alternate contractions at opposite ends.

In support of this hypothesis, protoplasmic drops from *Physarum* have been found to be contractile and it has become clear that the basis

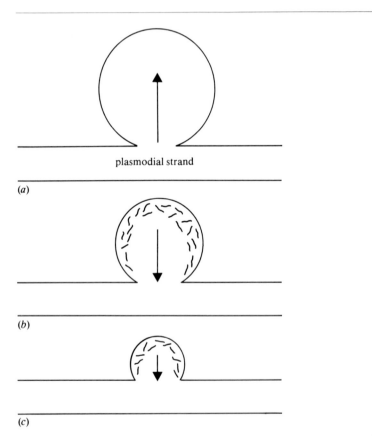

plasmodial strand

(*a*)

(*b*)

(*c*)

Fig. 4.4   Diagram to illustrate one of Wohlfarth-Bottermann's experiments with protoplasmic drops of *Physarum*. A drop is produced by puncturing the plasmodial strand (*a*). After a short while an extensive fibrillar network forms in the periphery of the drop (*b*) and contraction of this network results in the 'resorption' of the drop (*c*).

of this contractility resides in fibrillar elements.

Wohlfarth-Bottermann (1964) has shown that these are found only in the peripheral ectoplasmic layer, and then not as permanent differentiations, but as structures whose formation correlates temporally and spatially with the generation of motive force in the drop (Fig. 4.4). A similar situation also exists in the intact strands, since it is only at the pole of protoplasmic efflux that the ectoplasm becomes crowded with fibrils.

Consequently, a shortening of individual fibrils results in an overall condensation of the whole network and because of their arrangement, a decrease in the diameter of the ectoplasmic tube. This constriction exerts an hydraulic pressure on the endoplasmic fluid which leads to streaming. It must be stressed that the contractile apparatus is only transient, and contractions are not confined to a single region of a plasmodial strand but occur at successive points along its length – thus reinforcing the flow.

The overall picture is therefore one of assembly and disassembly of fibres correlated with contraction and relaxation respectively. The fibrils which make up the changing patterns of the contractile networks are composed of two types of filaments. Most obvious, are microfilaments of 8 nm diameter (Fig. 4.5) which have been shown to be composed of actin by HMM binding (Allera *et al.*, 1971) and immunofluorescence. Thicker filaments of 13–26 nm have also been detected in *Physarum*, but only in glycerinated preparations. This may reflect the relatively low proportion of myosin to actin in this system, and perhaps significantly, the presence of myosin filaments even in smooth muscle has only been noted fairly recently. Smaller filaments of 2–5 nm have also been observed, and some have interpreted these as monomeric myosin. However, the actual state of myosin in living cytoplasm of *Physarum* is unclear. It is not yet known whether myosin is involved in contraction either as an oligomer or as assembled myosin filaments, although synthetic myosin filaments, comparable to those of striated muscle, can be induced to form in actomyosin extracts (Nachmias, 1974).

Despite the uncertainty over whether assembled myosin filaments are involved in the normal contraction cycle, studies have shown that the oscillating contractions are dependent on the formation and breakdown of fibrils resulting from cyclic transformation of G- $\rightleftharpoons$ F-actin and the parallel association and subsequent dissociation of F-actin chains (Isenberg and Wohlfarth-Bottermann, 1976).

As in the case of muscle, the level of free Ca^{2+} is important in the regulation of motility. In plasmodia, the generation of motive force is decreased by calcium chelators, which lower the level of calcium, and it has been demonstrated that the ATPase activity of plasmodial actomyosin is stimulated by Ca^{2+}. Perhaps most significantly, factors

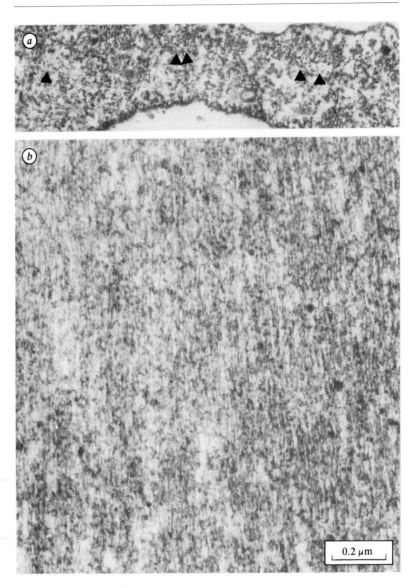

Fig. 4.5 Transverse section (*a*) and longitudinal section (*b*) of actomyosin fibrils in a protoplasmic strand of *Physarum* fixed at the start of contraction. The strands can be seen to be composed of aligned microfilaments (*b*) which appear as 6 nm dots in transverse section as shown by arrows (*a*). (From K. E. Wohlfarth-Bottermann and M. Fleischer, *Cell Tiss. Res.*, **165**, 327 (1976).)

similar to the troponin–tropomyosin complex of muscle have been isolated from *Physarum,* and appear to be involved in mediating the effect of calcium. The actual threshold concentration of Ca^{2+} in plasmodia is comparable to that for muscle (between 10^{-7} and 10^{-5} M), and as with muscle, membrane-bound compartments exist which are capable of accumulating Ca^{2+} – thus retaining the calcium concentration below the threshold level. Consequently, shuttle streaming could be accounted for by the alternate release and uptake of Ca^{2+} by the vacuolar system at opposing ends of plasmodial strands (Fig. 4.6), and such changes have been detected following the microinjection of the calcium-specific photoprotein aequorin (Ridgway and Durham, 1976).

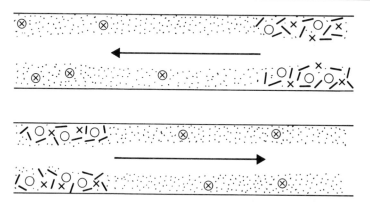

Fig. 4.6   Diagram showing shuttle streaming in protoplasmic strands of *Physarum*. The rods represent fibrils which form and contract in regions of efflux. The contraction appears dependent upon the levels of calcium (X) which is thought to be released from vacuoles. (Redrawn from H. Komnick, W. Stockem and K. E. Wohlfarth-Bottermann, *Int. Rev. Cytol.*, **34**, 169 (1973).)

4.3   Amoeboid movements

In amoeboid movement protoplasmic streaming is linked with locomotion of the cells themselves. Cell movements of this type which are typical of free living amoebae are not confined to the protozoa since they are also an important feature of a variety of metazoan cells, both in the living organism and in culture. In fact, encompassed within the term amoeboid movement, there is a considerable range of variation, ranging from lobose pseudopodia of fresh water amoebae to the fan-shaped ruffled pseudopodia of many cultured cells. The phenomenon of amoeboid movement has nevertheless been most extensively studied in *Amoeba proteus* and in species of the giant amoeba *Chaos,* and current theories of amoeboid movement have mainly derived from investigations of these protozoans. It must be stressed, however, that quite different mechanisms might exist in other amoebae.

4.3.1 Locomotion of *Amoeba proteus* and *Chaos* sp.

The streaming of cytoplasm in *Amoeba* and *Chaos* is accompanied by the extension of finger-like lobose pseudopodia which can be regarded as temporary locomotor organelles. The anterior end of a pseudopodium is occupied by a region free of granules, known as the hyaline cap, and this is continuous with a thin hyaline layer which completely surrounds the cell (Fig. 4.7). Beneath the hyaline layer is a granular ectoplasm which forms an ectoplasmic tube around the streaming endoplasm. During amoeboid movement the cytoplasm of an amoeba circulates continuously through the inner and outer regions of the cell. The endoplasm streams forwards until it reaches the hyaline cap, whereupon it diverges producing a 'fountain pattern'. It is at this point that there is an interconversion of sol-like endoplasm into gel-like ectoplasm, while the reverse situation occurs at the tail or uroid of the cell, as in this region the ectoplasm leaves the periphery and is 'recruited' to join the streaming endoplasm.

Investigations into the mechanism of such movements have involved physiological studies into the motile properties of intact amoebae and

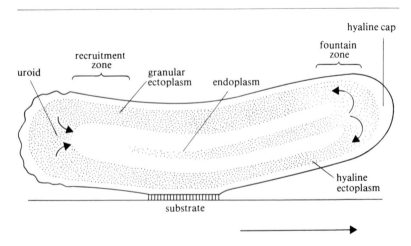

Fig. 4.7 Diagram illustrating patterns of cytoplasmic streaming during amoeboid movement. The arrow denotes the direction of movement.

also cytoplasmic extracts, together with morphological examination of the cytoplasmic structure. Such approaches have resulted in the almost general agreement that the movement is based upon contractility. On the one hand, it has been shown that glycerinated amoebae undergo contraction on the addition of ATP and Mg^{++}, while on the other hand studies have demonstrated that cytoplasm isolated from amoebae retained remarkably similar motile properties to those of the intact cell.

After harvesting cytoplasmic extracts of *Amoeba proteus* by means of centrifugation, Thompson and Wolpert (1963) discovered that at 4°C they exhibited only Brownian movement, but that if ATP was added and the cytoplasm allowed to warm to 22°C, the extracts became motile. Initially small oscillatory movements were observed, with the displacement of the granules gradually increasing until whole regions moved as single blocks and even showed overall twitching. Eventually some streams of granules became arranged in parallel lines moving in opposite directions through the cytoplasm over distances as great as 600 μm. Alternatively, in other preparations the granules ceased to move in directed streams, but whole areas appeared to gel into sheets which contracted, thus trapping and drawing together the granules. Ultrastructural studies of such extracts at 22°C in the presence of ATP have revealed two distinct types of filaments (Pollard and Ito, 1970) – thin 5–8 nm filaments and thicker 16 nm filaments. Unlike the thick filaments which could be seen throughout, the presence of the thin filaments proved to be dependent upon temperature, since they were not observed in extracts at 4°C, but only on warming. Furthermore, their formation closely correlated with movement in the extract and an increase in its viscosity. Such findings were interpreted as suggesting that variations in the consistency of the amoeba cytoplasm may be directly related to the proportion of filament precursors polymerised into filaments.

Filaments seen in cytoplasmic extracts had previously proved most elusive in the intact cells, and were apparently destroyed by fixatives which normally preserved the general cell morphology. However, by exposing cells to the dye alcian blue and by using unbuffered rather than alkaline osmium solutions, Nachmias (1964, 1968) was able to observe both thick and thin filaments in the cytoplasm of *Chaos*. Also, by tearing open the plasmalemma with fine hairs and by injecting fixatives directly into the cytoplasm, it was possible to overcome one of the major problems – the lack of penetration of the fixative.

The presence of thick and thin filaments in motile extracts and intact amoebae suggested that they were the contractile elements within the cytoplasm. In support of this hypothesis, the thin filaments resemble F-actin in size, and have been identified as such in motile cytoplasmic extracts of *Amoeba* on the basis of their characteristic binding of HMM

(Pollard and Korn, 1971). The same technique has been employed for identifying and localising thin filaments *in situ* within the giant amoeba *Chaos* (Comly, 1973), and has shown that microfilaments exist both in the vesicular cytoplasm, where streaming normally occurs, and in the ectoplasmic layer in apparent association with the plasma membrane. Such findings naturally led to speculation that the thick filaments might be myosin and indeed proteins which comigrate with actin and myosin on SDS–polyacrylamide gels have since been found in the cytoplasm of *Chaos*. In addition, and intriguingly, the morphology of the thick filaments as seen by negative staining is identical to those in striated muscle and in *Physarum*.

The significance of examining the properties of isolated amoeba cytoplasm has increased considerably since Taylor *et al.* (1973) succeeded in isolating the cytoplasm in a lifelike condition from *Chaos* by rupturing the plasma membrane using the tip of a micropipette and collecting the cytoplasm in physiological medium. Such a technique has the advantage that the chemical environment can then be controlled and the effect on the contractility and the streaming of isolated cytoplasm can be examined. Cytoplasm isolated into 'stabilisation solution' (see Table 4.1) was non-motile but contained numerous fibrils of $0.1 - 0.4$ μm diameter which could be seen most clearly when the cytoplasm was stretched. Stretching of the cytoplasm in this way brought about an increase in its birefringence, indicative of ordered structure, and also illustrated its elastic properties. When the stretched stabilised cytoplasm was then subjected to 'contraction solution' which differed from the stabilising solution mainly in its calcium

Table 4.1 Solutions used to isolate, stabilise and control the motility of *Amoeba* cytoplasm (from Taylor *et al.*, 1973).

	Stabilisation solution	Contraction solution	Relaxation solution	Flare solution
pH	7.0	7.0	7.0	7.0
mosM	85–100	85–100	85–100	85–100
Ionic strength (±0.01)	0.05	0.05	0.05	0.05
Pipes buffer mM	5.0	5.0	5.0	5.0
Dipotassium EGTA mM	5.0	5.0	5.0	5.0
Disodium ATP mM	0	0	1.0	0.5
KCl mM	27.0	27.0	27.0	27.0
NaCl mM	3.0	3.0	3.0	3.0
CaCl₂ mM	0	4.5	0	4.2
MgCl₂	0	0	0	0.5
Free Ca⁺⁺	$<10^{-7}$M	*c.* 1.0×10^{-6}M	$<10^{-7}$M	*c.* 7.0×10^{-7}M

concentration (see Table 4.1), this brought about contraction of the visible fibres which broadened as they became shorter. Conversely, stabilised cytoplasm treated with 'relaxation solution' gradually lost its birefringence and viscoelasticity – further showing that the state of contraction is dependent upon the level of calcium ions present. These findings appeared at first to be contradictory to all the previous observations which had shown that streaming and contraction in cytoplasmic extracts were either inhibited by calcium or lacked calcium sensitivity, but required Mg^{++} and ATP instead. The anomaly has since been resolved, however, with the demonstration of the loss of calcium sensitivity during the glycerination process. The significant outcome from studies of this nature is the discovery that solutions which are capable of controlling contractility in striated muscle, also bring about the rigor (stabilised), contracted and relaxed states in isolated amoeba cytoplasm.

Electron microscopy of stabilised, contracted and relaxed cytoplasm has been carried out, and while both thick and thin filaments are discernible in unstretched cytoplasm, distinct oriented arrays of filaments are only seen in stretched preparations, as one might expect from the birefringence seen in the light microscope. On contraction, however, the filaments pack and lose their orientation (compare Fig. 4.8a, b) while in the relaxed state there again appears to be no association between the different filaments.

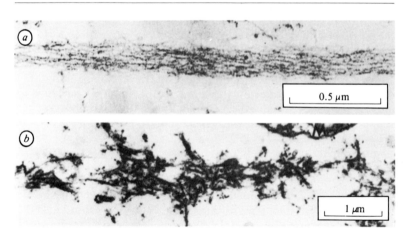

Fig. 4.8 Electron micrographs of cytoplasm isolated from *Chaos* in the stabilised (a) and contracted (b) states. The former shows predominantly 7 nm actin microfilaments while the latter is characterised by a disorganised array of both actin and myosin filaments. (From R. D. Allen and D. L. Taylor, in *Molecules and Cell Movement*, p. 239, Raven Press, N.Y. (1975).)

Although widely accepted as being based upon contractility, the question as to how this leads to movement of amoebae remains paramount, and there are a number of theories to explain this. The ectoplasmic tube contraction theory, first proposed by Mast (1925) and expanded by others, envisaged that contractions in the uroid of the cell exerted a pressure on the endoplasm which is *pushed* to regions of lower pressure, namely the pseudopodia. By contrast, the frontal contraction theory of Allen (1961) proposes that contraction occurs in the endoplasm at the anterior advancing end of the cell and that this is manifested by the conversion of endoplasmic sol into ectoplasmic gel and consequently a *pulling* forwards of the endoplasmic core. With the outline of these theories in mind, let us consider the evidence for and against each.

Ectoplasmic tube contraction theory   The ectoplasmic tube contraction theory attributed streaming, as with *Physarum*, to a pressure gradient, resulting in this case from contraction in the uroid. This was supported largely by the experiments of Kamiya who adapted his double-chamber method to amoebae and established the existence of a small pressure gradient within the cells. Also in favour of ectoplasmic tail contraction is the claim that filaments have been observed predominantly in the ectoplasmic cortex in the uroid of the cell. Reports too that a continual folding of the plasma membrane occurs at the posterior end were again interpreted as resulting from ectoplasmic contraction.

Contrary to such an hypothesis are the findings of Allen *et al.* (1971) who postulated that if a pressure gradient were responsible for the observed flow, then reversal of that gradient should reverse its direction. They tested this by applying suction to the uroid of advancing amoebae but with little effect on the streaming and extension of pseudopodia. Furthermore, as they pointed out, new pseudopod tips are usually the very site where one first observes streaming – an observation which is difficult to account for by contraction at the tail.

Another feature which is hard to reconcile with a pressure gradient hypothesis is the demonstration of streaming in isolated cytoplasmic extracts with no cell membrane nor the normal ectoplasm/endoplasm relationship. It has been shown too, that treatment of cytoplasmic extracts with a so-called 'flare solution' (see Table 4.1) caused naked cytoplasm to extend pseudopodial-like structures which are loop shaped in appearance and remarkably comparable in both dimensions and streaming rate to the fountain streaming in intact pseudopodia (Fig. 4.9).

Frontal contraction model   The frontal contraction model for

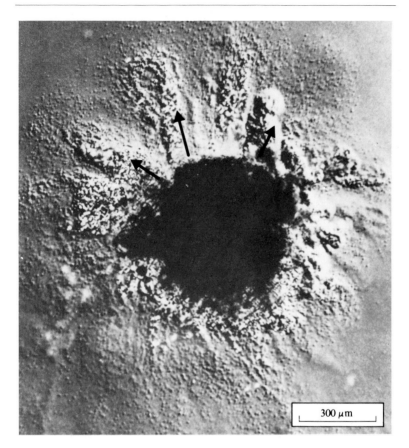

Fig. 4.9 A cytoplasmic droplet from the giant amoeba *Chaos carolinensis* in 'flare' solution. Under these conditions the droplet extends pseudopodia-like loops of cytoplasm (arrows). (From D. L. Taylor, *et al.* (1973).)

amoeboid movement interprets the changes in consistency of the cytoplasm from gel to sol and vice versa in terms of a contraction–relaxation phenomenon, and much of the evidence in favour of the model derives from direct comparisons between the properties of cytoplasm *in situ* with those of isolated cytoplasm (Fig. 4.10). For example, it has been shown that while the endoplasm is birefringent, birefringence is lost as it approaches the tips of the pseudopodia and becomes part of the ectoplasmic tube – just as has been observed on contraction of isolated cytoplasm. The assumption is that the ectoplasm then remains in the contracted state until it comes to

111

lie at the tail of the cell, where it reverts from a contracted to a relaxed state in a manner exhibited by cytoplasmic extracts. At this point the endoplasm streams forwards once again and gradually regains birefringence.

The model further proposed that the cytoplasmic events outlined for different regions of the cell could be explained by either of two hypotheses. The first envisages a calcium gradient between the anterior end and uniform levels of ATP throughout. The second is a two gradient hypothesis which incorporates a similar calcium gradient as the first, but in addition proposes a reverse gradient of ATP which is at higher concentrations in the tail. Such ideas have been tested by

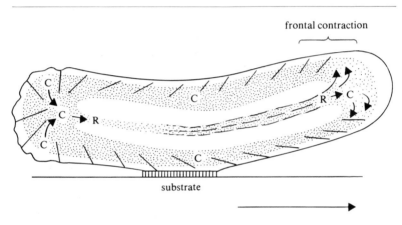

Fig. 4.10 Diagram of amoeboid movement showing cytoplasmic regions corresponding to different states of isolated cytoplasm. The endoplasm gains structure and contractility as it approaches the tip of a pseudopodium. The formation of ectoplasm in this region involves a transition from the relaxed to the contracted state (R→C). The ectoplasm remains in the contracted state (C) until it is recruited in the uroid region of the cell (C→R). (After D. L. Taylor, J. A. Rhodes and S. A. Hammond, *J. Cell Biol.*, **67**, 427a (1975).)

Allen and co-workers who microinjected their relaxing, contracting and stabilising solutions into different regions of intact *Chaos,* and while these go some way towards relating the behaviour of isolated cytoplasm to how movements within the cell are regulated, the actual presence of the supposed chemical gradients remains to be demonstrated.

Another feature which also remains in doubt, is that while the model proposes that the transition of endoplasm to ectoplasm is due to an interaction between actin and myosin, resulting in the formation of the ectoplasmic tube, it is not at all clear whether the converse situation at the tail is accompanied solely by a dissociation of actin filaments from myosin filaments, or a disassembly of the filaments themselves. Certainly conditions of high ionic strength as well as calcium ion concentrations below 10^{-7}M have been shown to disassemble the myosin and also the actin filaments. It remains to be determined, however, whether conditions of this sort exist in the living cell, such that polymerisation and depolymerisation of actin and/or myosin filaments, as well as their association and dissociation, are important.

4.3.2 Locomotion of cells in culture

As has previously been mentioned, the phenomenon of amoeboid movement is also exhibited by metazoan cells such as human leucocytes and fibroblasts, and not least importantly by cells showing morphogenetic cell movements during development. Since it is difficult to make direct observations of metazoan cells while within the organism, their movements are usually studied in the artificial conditions of cell and tissue culture.

When cells migrate in culture, they often extend flattened and sometimes fan-shaped *lamellipodia*, at the leading edge of which can be seen an undulating or 'ruffled' membrane (Abercrombie, 1961). During their locomotion, only small areas of cell surface actually touch and adhere to the culture dish. These contacts, which occur most prominently at the tips of the leading lamella, can be seen by means of scanning electron microscopy, but more clearly when cells are made to round up by the application of trypsin – a treatment which leaves retraction fibres attached at their distal ends by flattened pads (Revel *et al.*, 1974; Fig. 4.11*a*). It is at the attachment points of the leading lamella, just inside the cell membrane, that dense structures known as *plaques* form (Fig. 4.11*b*). From these plaques, bundles of microfilaments, making up quite sizeable fibres of 0.5–1.0 μm diameter and 100 μm in length, run backwards towards the posterior end of the cell where they seem to end free in the cytoplasm. A separate network of filaments also exists beneath the cell membrane, and microtubules are also occasionally seen in cell processes.

As points of adhesion are commonly found near the advancing edges of cells it has been assumed that locomotion results from a pulling of the microfilament bundles, consequently designated *stress fibres*, on these regions (Fig. 4.12*a*). The fibres themselves have been shown to contain actin by means of HMM binding, and both actin and myosin by immunofluorescence techniques (see Fig. 2.2*b*), suggesting that these contractile proteins are involved in the movement and contraction of tissue culture cells. Indirect evidence that the fibres participate in contraction derives from observations using polarising microscopy. This demonstrates that while the fibres are strongly birefringent, on adding ATP to glycerinated cells, they lose their birefringence,

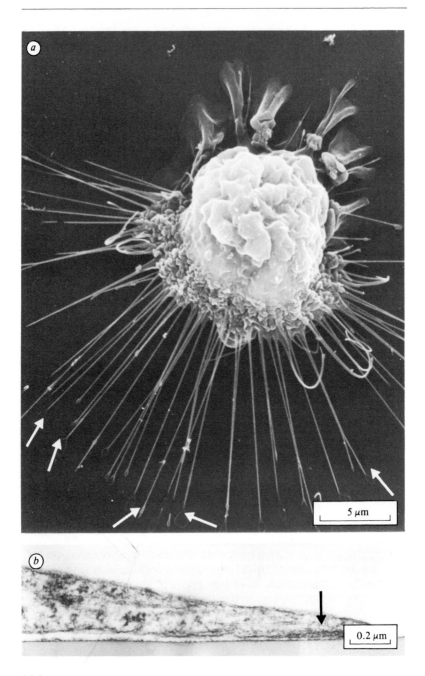

Fig. 4.11 Cell–substrate adhesion. (*a*) Cultured LA9 cell which has been treated in a way which caused it to round-up. The cell has left long retraction fibres still attached at their distal ends by large flattened pads (arrows), and these represent the attachment points of the cell to the substratum. (*b*) Vertical section of the leading lamella of a chick heart fibroblast showing a plaque structure (arrow) adjacent to the region of adhesion. ((*a*) is from J. P. Revel *et al.* (1974); (*b*) is from M. Abercrombie, J. E. M. Heaysman and S. M. Pegrum, *Exp. Cell Res.*, **67**, 359 (1971).)

indicating an alteration of molecular structure during contraction.

Studies using cytochalasin B have also been carried out with the intention of showing a relationship between locomotion and the cytoplasmic filaments, but due to the lack of knowledge regarding the precise mode of action of the drug (Section 2.4.4), the interpretation of the results from such studies has proved somewhat controversial. Cytochalasin undisputedly arrests motility, and the cells remain spread and flattened, demonstrating that the cessation of locomotion is not an indirect effect of the cells rounding up. By contrast, colchicine administered at levels high enough to disassemble microtubules had no effect on the ruffled membrane activity or on net cell movement.

There is now direct evidence for the active contraction of fibres, from the studies of Isenberg *et al.* (1976) who have cleverly isolated single fibres by laser microirradiation and demonstrated that they contract up to 60% in 30 seconds on adding solutions containing ATP (Fig. 4.12*b–d*).

Huxley has proposed a model for the locomotion of tissue culture cells (Fig. 4.13) based on the fact that when moving over a substrate one part of the cell must be anchored while other parts move relative to it. The model equates the sites of attachment of microfilaments, or stress fibres, with the Z lines of striated muscle. Filaments trailing back from this are regarded as one component of an active shearing system, other components in the cytoplasm flowing forward over the attached filaments. During one cycle, therefore, the front region of the cell is extended as a result of pressure generated by cytoplasmic streaming, the attachment sites are laid down, actin filaments polymerise onto these and shearing forces are developed in the cytoplasm. The initial contraction results then in the characteristic ruffling, but when the attachment sites are securely anchored the cell is pulled forwards.

This model is supported by observations of virally transformed cells, a curious feature of which is their altered substrate adhesion and locomotion. For example, studies have shown that the undersides of baby hamster kidney cells (BHK cells), transformed with polyoma virus, possess few regions of cell substrate attachment and also few bundles of microfilaments. They have less actin associated with their cell surface than the normal cells from which they were derived, and it seems likely that the altered adhesive and locomotory properties of

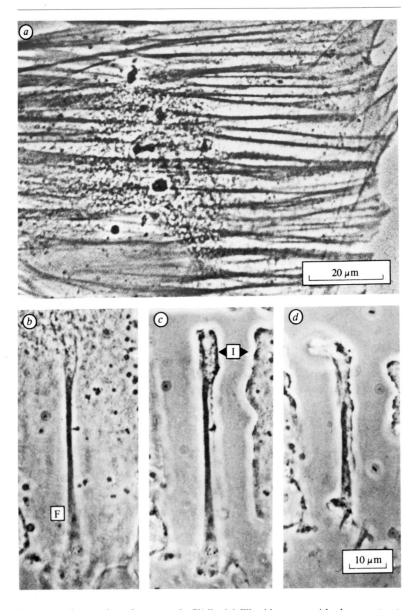

Fig. 4.12 Contraction of actomyosin fibrils. (*a*) Fibroblast seen with phase contrast optics showing many actomyosin fibrils (stress fibres) arranged parallel to the long axis of the cell body. (*b*)–(*d*) Series showing an actomyosin fibril (F) within the cell (*b*), isolated from the cytoplasm by laser microdissection (*c*), and the contraction it undergoes after adding medium containing ATP (*d*). (From G. Isenberg *et al.* (1976).)

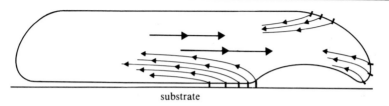

substrate

Fig. 4.13 Diagrammatic representation of a sliding filament mechanism proposed by H. E. Huxley to explain cell movement. The mechanism is based upon shearing forces developed between two populations of antipolar filaments, one associated with the cell surface and the other free in the cytoplasm. The cell extends and forms new attachment points as it moves from left to right. (After H. E. Huxley, (1973).)

transformed cells may arise from their inability to organise adhesion plaques and microfilament bundles.

4.4 Brush border contraction

Although many current models of cell motility assume a sliding filament mechanism involving the interaction of actin and myosin filaments, in no case has the organisation of these components into a structure which resembles the muscle sarcomere been described. This is possibly because structures such as the stress fibres in migrating fibroblasts, and the actomyosin fibrils in the ectoplasm of *Physarum* are ephemeral, and activities such as membrane ruffling and shuttle streaming appear to involve a continuous turnover of actin filaments. By contrast, in this section we shall consider a motile process which, like muscle, performs repeated movements at a specific location in the cell.

The surface of intestinal epithelium is characterised by the presence of densely packed microvilli to form the so-called *brush border* (Fig. 4.14). Although it is only poorly described, the microvilli are evidently capable of some form of cyclic movement, possibly taking the form of rapid beating. Ultrastructural studies of the brush border reveal a clear potential for movement. Each microvillus of chicken intestinal epithelium is between 1–2 μm in length, 0.1 μm in diameter and contains a core of between 20–30 microfilaments (Fig. 4.14a). At the tip of the microvillus this core is embedded in a dense membrane-associated matrix, while at the base it extends beyond the microvillus into a terminal web containing thick myosin-like filaments, often connecting with the microfilaments of adjacent microvilli (Mooseker and Tilney, 1975).

The filaments of the core exhibit irregular bridging to each other, but distinct periodic bridging to the microvillar membrane

117

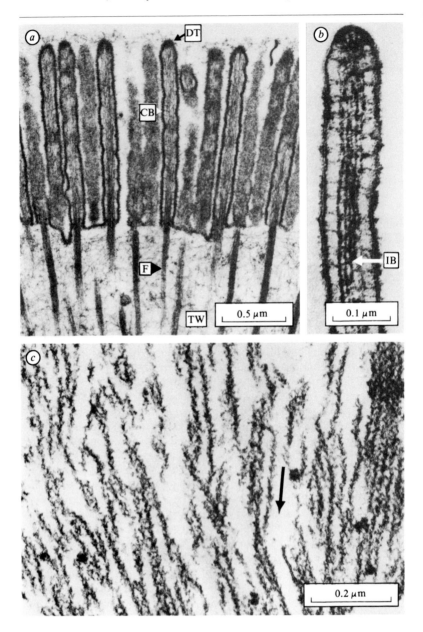

Fig. 4.14 Microfilaments in the brush border. (*a*) Brush border from chicken intestinal epithelium. The microvilli each contain a core of actin filaments (F) that extend into a terminal web (TW), while the tips of the filaments are embedded in a dense matrix (DT).

In some regions cross-bridges (CB) can be seen between the filaments and the outer membrane. (*b*) Higher magnification of a microvillus showing that bridges (IB) also occur between the filaments themselves. (*c*) Demembranated brush border decorated with HMM. The arrowhead complexes all point towards the terminal web (arrow). (From M. S. Mooseker and L. G. Tilney (1975).)

(Fig. 4.14*b*). Both these bridges and the dense material into which the microfilaments insert at the tip exhibit a positive reaction to antibody produced against muscle α actinin, a major protein of muscle Z lines. This protein, together with actin, myosin and possibly also tropomyosin, has also been identified in isolated brush borders analysed by gel electrophoresis.

Isolated brush borders, demembranated with Triton X-100, retain their characteristic organisation and allow decoration by HMM fragment S1 (Fig. 4.14*c*). Such treatment has shown that all the filaments of the core reveal the same polarity with the S1 arrowheads pointing away from the anchorage point of the filaments in the membrane at the tip of the microvillus (which contains α actinin) in the same way that decorated filaments in muscle point away from the Z line. To continue the analogy with muscle one step further, such an arrangement predicts that any movement would occur in the direction pointed by the arrowheads, i.e. towards the terminal web. Demembranated brush borders in the presence of Ca^{2+} and ATP exhibited a rapid (< 1 second) contraction, the core of the microfilaments plunging basally towards and through the web (Mooseker, 1976). Some of the marginal filaments of the core were seen to splay laterally on contraction, into the terminal web, but the majority remained together as a bundle.

On the basis of these observations Mooseker and Tilney (1975) have proposed a model for brush border contraction where any pair of adjacent microvilli can be regarded as forming a sarcomere (Fig. 4.15). Bipolar myosin filaments in the terminal web interact with microfilaments of opposed polarity, evidently from adjacent microvilli as all the filaments within a single microvillus exhibit the same polarity. The model requires only a proportion of the filaments of the core to participate in the myosin interaction, presumably those observed to splay during contraction, the bridges between microfilaments being responsible for the contraction of the core as a unit. These observations leave unanswered how the movement observed *in vitro* relates to the movements of the living cell and also how contraction is reversed (the polarity of the actin filaments prevents this also being an actin–myosin interaction). However, they provide a beautiful demonstration of the organisation of a permanent cellular contractile system and the role of membranes in the anchorage and possibly determination of growth of actin filaments.

119

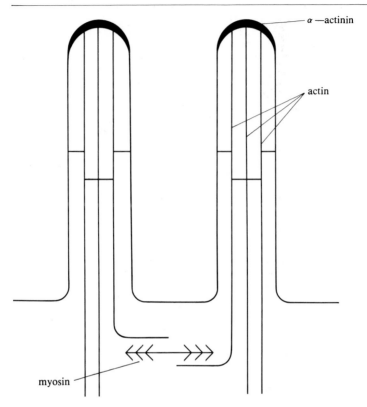

Fig. 4.15 Model proposed by Mooseker and Tilney showing the sarcomeric-like functional organisation of actin and myosin in the brush border. (After M. S. Mooseker and L. G. Tilney (1975).)

References

ABERCROMBIE, M. (1961) The bases of the locomotory behaviour of fibroblasts, *Exp. Cell Res. Suppl.,* **8,** 188–200.

ALLEN, R. D. (1961) A new theory of amoeboid movement and protoplasmic streaming, *Exp. Cell Res. Suppl.,* **8,** 17–31.

ALLEN, R. D., FRANCIS, D. and ZEH, R. (1971) Direct test of the positive pressure gradient theory of pseudopod extension and retraction in amoebae, *Science,* **174,** 1237–40.

ALLERA, A., BECK, R. and WOHLFARTH-BOTTERMANN, K. E. (1971) Extensive fibrillar protoplasmic differentiations and their significance for protoplasmic streaming, *Cytobiologie,* **4,** 437–49.

COMLY, L. T. (1973) Microfilaments in *Chaos carolinensis.* Membrane association, distribution and heavy meromyosin binding in the glycerinated cell, *J. Cell Biol.,* **58,** 230–7.

References

HUXLEY, H. E. (1973) Muscular contraction and cell motility, *Nature*, **243**, 445–9.

ISENBERG, G., RATHKE, P. C., HÜLSMANN, N., FRANKE, W. W. and WOHLFARTH-BOTTERMANN, K. E. (1976) Cytoplasmic actomyosin fibrils in tissue culture cells, *Cell Tiss. Res.*, **166**, 427–43.

ISENBERG, G. and WOHLFARTH-BOTTERMANN, K. E. (1976) Transformation of cytoplasmic actin. Importance for the organization of the contractile gel reticulum – relaxation cycle of cytoplasmic actomyosin, *Cell Tiss. Res.*, **173**, 495–528.

KAMIYA, N. (1959) Protoplasmic streaming, *Plasmatologia*, **8**, 1–199.

LOEWY, A. G. (1952) An actomyosin-like substance from the plasmodium of a myxomycete, *J. Cell Comp. Physiol.*, **40**, 127–56.

MAST, S. O. (1925) Structure, movement, locomotion and stimulation in amoeba, *J. Morph.*, **41**, 347–425.

MOOSEKER, M. S. (1976) Brush border motility. Microvillar contraction in triton-treated brush borders isolated from intestinal epithelium, *J. Cell Biol.*, **71**, 417–33.

MOOSEKER, M. S. and TILNEY, L. G. (1975) The organization of an actin filament–membrane complex: filament polarity and membrane attachment in the microvilli of intestinal epithelial cells, *J. Cell Biol.*, **67**, 725–43.

NACHMIAS, V. T. (1964) Fibrillar structures in the cytoplasm of *Chaos chaos*, *J. Cell Biol.*, **23**, 183–8.

NACHMIAS, V. T. (1968) Further electron microscope studies on fibrillar organization of the ground cytoplasm of *Chaos chaos*, *J. Cell Biol.*, **38**, 40–50.

NACHMIAS, V. T. (1974) Properties of *Physarum* myosin purified by a potassium iodide procedure, *J. Cell Biol.*, **62**, 54–65.

POLLARD, T. D. and ITO, S. (1970) Cytoplasmic filaments of *Amoeba proteus*. I. The role of filaments in consistency changes and movement, *J. Cell Biol.*, **46**, 267–89.

POLLARD, T. D. and KORN, E. D. (1971) Filaments of *Amoeba proteus*. II. Binding of heavy meromyosin by thin filaments in motile cytoplasmic extracts, *J. Cell Biol.*, **48**, 216–9.

REVEL, J. P., HOCH, P. and HO, D. (1974) Adhesion of culture cells to their substratum, *Exp. Cell Res.*, **84**, 207–18.

RIDGWAY, E. B. and DURHAM, A. C. H. (1976) Oscillations of calcium ion concentration in *Physarum polycephalum*, *J. Cell Biol.*, **69**, 223–6.

SEIFRIZ, W. (1943) Protoplasmic streaming, *Bot. Rev.*, **9**, 49–123.

TAYLOR, D. L., CONDEELIS, J. S., MOORE, P. L. and ALLEN, R. D. (1973) The contractile basis of amoeboid movement. I. The chemical control of motility in isolated cytoplasm, *J. Cell Biol.*, **59**, 378–94.

THOMPSON, C. M. and WOLPERT, L. (1963) The isolation of motile cytoplasm from *Amoeba proteus*, *Exp. Cell Res.*, **32**, 156–60.

TILNEY, L. G. (1975a) Actin filaments in the acrosomal reaction of *Limulus* sperm. Motion generated by alterations in the packing of the filaments, *J. Cell Biol.*, **64**, 289–310.

TILNEY, L. G. (1975b) The role of actin in nonmuscle cell motility, in *Molecules and Cell Movement*, eds S. Inoué and R. E. Stephens. Raven Press, N.Y.

TILNEY, L. G. (1976a) The polymerization of actin. II. How nonfilamentous actin becomes nonrandomly distributed in sperm: evidence for the association of this actin with membranes, *J. Cell Biol.*, **69**, 51–7.

TILNEY, L. G. (1976b) III. Aggregates of nonfilamentous actin and its associated proteins, *J. Cell Biol.*, **69**, 73–89.

WOHLFARTH-BOTTERMANN, K. E. (1964) Differentiations of the ground cytoplasm and their significance for the generation of the motive force of amoeboid movement, in *Primitive Motile Systems in Cell Biology*, pp. 79–109, eds R. D. Allen and N. Kamiya. Academic Press, N.Y.

121

Chapter 5

Movement within cells

Intracellular transport and protoplasmic streaming are both examples of movement within cells. The former is seen most obviously in large asymmetric animal cells and occurs along tracts of cytoplasmic microtubules. Protoplasmic streaming, on the other hand, is exhibited by a variety of plant cells, is more rapid, and appears based upon microfilaments.

5.1 Intracellular transport and microtubules

Microtubules have been associated with the intracellular transport of a variety of cell components in a wide range of systems. The association stems from ultrastructural observations of microtubules in regions exhibiting cytoplasmic movement, usually along cell extensions or cell processes within which the microtubules are invariably arranged parallel to the direction of movement. In addition to their possible involvement in motility it is clear that in many cases the microtubules are important in the actual development and maintenance of the cell asymmetry.

Components which move along microtubular tracts range from whole nuclei, chromosomes (see chapter on mitosis), pigment granules in chromatophores, particles in the axopodia of heliozoan protozoans, ribosomes in insect ovaries, and a wide variety of less well characterised vesicles and inclusions in other cells, to a general cytoplasmic flow such as occurs along nerve axons. Some intracellular motile systems, particularly those which lend themselves to observation and experimentation, have received considerable attention and will be described as examples.

5.1.1 Examples of microtubule associated intracellular transport

Axopodia of heliozoans Protozoans of the order Heliozoa possess numerous slender radiating cytoplasmic processes called *axopodia* (Fig. 5.1*a*). These apparently rigid structures are only a few microns in diameter but protrude almost 0.5 mm from the cell body. Early studies with the light microscope revealed that each axopodium contained a strongly birefringent core or axoneme running its entire length (McKinnon, 1909) and that this consisted of parallel fibres (Roskin, 1925). Such fibres were shown to be hollow by means of electron microscopy (Kitching, 1964) and to be arranged in two sheets integrated to form a double coil around a central axis. Following this, using improved fixation techniques, Tilney and Porter (1965) carried out detailed ultrastructural studies of the elaborate and characteristic patterns of microtubules in axopodia of a number of genera.

In *Actinosphaerium, Echinosphaerium* and also *Actinophrys*, the most studied species, the two sheets of axonemal microtubules are spirally interwound, and joined by a series of tangential, radial and secondary cross-links (Fig. 5.1*b*). Furthermore, the links of the double spiral are such that an axoneme appears divided into a number of distinct triangular sectors when viewed in cross-section. The axonemal microtubules decrease in number from approximately 500 at the base of the axoneme, to 5 at the tip, and the axopodia themselves taper correspondingly.

During the movement of the organisms, the axopodia change in length in an apparently coordinated fashion. Since similar changes in axopodial length can be brought about experimentally by treatments known to depolymerise microtubules, this is regarded as evidence that the microtubular axoneme acts as support for the axopodia.

In addition to the changes in length, cytoplasmic streaming has been observed within axopodia, and their geometry makes them ideally suitable for a study of intracellular movement. MacDonald and Kitching (1967) have reported between six and twelve independently moving longitudinal streams of protoplasm around the axoneme and suggested that the sectors of secondary tubules might drive the streams peristaltically. Indeed, since the microtubules which make up the axonemes are the only obvious linear components present in the axopodia, they were considered as likely candidates for a role in the observed motility.

The assumption that the microtubule axoneme is involved in the movement along axopodia has been ingeniously investigated by Edds (1975a, b). By creating artificial axopodia in which a glass rod was

123

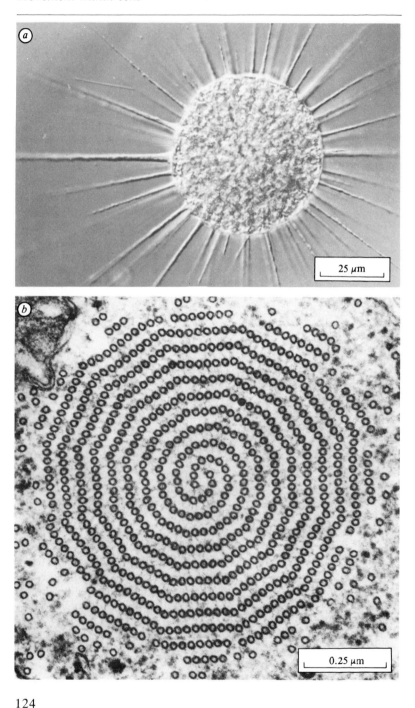

Fig. 5.1 Heliozoan axopodia. (*a*) Nomarski interference contrast micrograph of the heliozoan *Actinophrys sol* showing the radial arrangement of the axopodia. (*b*) Electron micrograph of a transverse section through an axopodium showing the intricate pattern of microtubules which comprise the central axoneme. ((*a*) is from C. D. Ockleford and J. B. Tucker, *J. Ultrastruct. Res.*, **44**, 369 (1973); (*b*) is courtesy of L. E. Roth and Y. Shigenaka.)

substituted for the microtubule axoneme, he was able to show that the movement of particles in artificial and natural axopodia was similar. In some regions many particles moved in the same direction at the same velocity, while in other regions there was either no movement at all, or movement in the opposite direction. In all cases, the movement was intermittent but the average distance travelled in one continuous movement was 3.1 ± 2.5 μm at an average velocity of 0.66 ± 0.32 μm s^{-1}.

Because normal particle movement occurred in artificial axopodia where glass axonemes had replaced the microtubule axonemes, and because levels of colchicine which cause normal axopodia to collapse had no effect on the movement along artificial axopodia, Edds was able to conclude that the microtubules of the axoneme act only as structural supports for the axopodium, and not as units for the generation of motive force.

Movement of pigment granules in fish chromatophores　Fish, as do many animals, exhibit striking colour changes in response to different background illumination. The colour changes are affected by changes in the distribution of pigment granules in single cells known as *chromatophores*, whose behaviour is under neurohumoral or hormonal control.

Perhaps the most extensively studied is the fish melanophore which is a highly asymmetrical star-shaped cell containing black melanin granules which disperse outwards into the long cell processes and aggregate within the cell body (Fig. 5.2*a*). The granules themselves are membrane-bound ovoid bodies of 0.4–0.7 μm in length and are ordered into columns within the cell processes (Fig. 5.2*b*).

The movement of the melanin granules is clearly selective, since neither nuclei nor mitochondria migrate in conjunction with the granules. Their movement has been extensively studied by Green (1968) who reported distinct differences in the manner and velocity of movement during dispersal and aggregation. During dispersal the granules showed a discontinuous to-and-fro movement in which individual granules moved independently of each other over distances of 0.8–4.0 μm in such a way that granules took up to one minute to cover a distance of 2 μm. By contrast, the aggregation is a continuous process, and considerably more rapid, with movement over distances of up to 60 μm at 5 μm s^{-1}. The stimuli for aggregation and dispersal

125

are also different, and it is not known yet whether the mechanisms involved are the same.

Numerous ultrastructural studies have shown that these pigment migrations occur in close proximity to a large number of microtubules (Fig. 5.2c). The microtubules are oriented within, and parallel to, the long axis of the melanophore processes, where they exist as a cortical set around a central set. A few microfilaments also exist in some fish chromatophores but are not considered important in pigment migration, although the same may not be true for amphibians where microfilaments abound.

To determine whether the microtubules are required for pigment motility there have been many studies in which melanophores have been subjected to low temperatures, high hydrostatic pressure and a variety of antimitotic agents, all known to depolymerise microtubules in other systems. Both cold and high pressure brought about a loss of alignment and a cessation of movement of the pigment granules, but on reversion to normal conditions the granules realigned from the cell body outwards and recommenced typical movements (Murphy and Tilney, 1974). A similar effect has been observed on subjecting cells to a relatively high concentration of colchicine.

Such experiments clearly show that the microtubules are essential for movement in this system, and there are two possible explanations for this. Either the microtubules could push/pull the pigment granules through the cytoplasm of the melanophore processes as the result of their assembly and disassembly; or alternatively the granules could move or glide actively along a fixed microtubule framework.

In attempts to investigate these possibilities, conflicting reports have arisen as to the arrangements of microtubules in the chromatophore processes of different species. Porter (1973) has reported that during pigment aggregation in erythrophores of *Holocentrus* the microtubules of the central apparatus, but not the cell cortex, depolymerise and there have been similar reports of a reduction of 30% in the numbers of microtubules in melanophore processes of *Pterophyllum*. Such evidence does indeed suggest the possibility that the motive force for granule aggregation might be provided by a depolymerisation of the central microtubules. By contrast, however, a depletion in the number of microtubules on aggregation does not occur in *Fundulus* (Murphy and Tilney, 1974) and such conflicting evidence

Fig. 5.2 Melanophores of teleost fish. (*a*) The pigment in the melanophores on the left is dispersed throughout the cell processes whereas that on the right is aggregated. (*b*) Micrograph of a melanophore with the pigment dispersed showing rows of pigment granules in the cell processes. (*c*) Transverse section of a melanophore process showing the dense pigment granules and many microtubules. (From D. B. Murphy and L. G. Tilney (1974).)

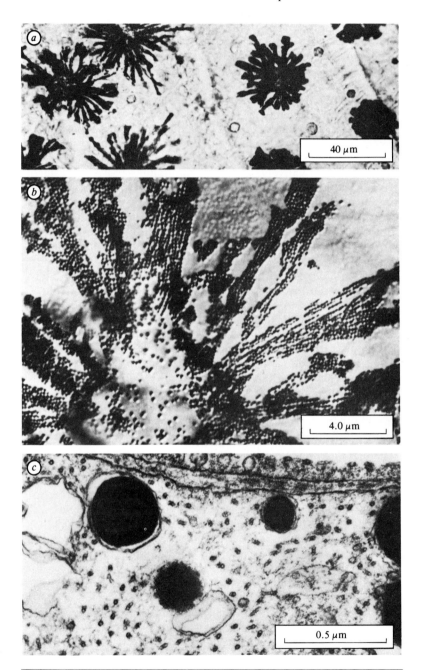

is difficult to reconcile. Murphy and Tilney suggest that the variance might be accounted for by differences in the species examined or due to differences in response to fixation. They also point out that since melanophore processes of *Fundulus* can be severed from the rest of the cell, and that pigment can then be induced to aggregate and disperse normally, even in the presence of levels of colchicine which would bind to and prevent polymerisation of microtubules, a mechanism based on polymerisation is unlikely.

Murphy and Tilney consider that since the number and arrangement of microtubules in melanophore processes, of *Fundulus* at any rate, remain unchanged during aggregation of pigment, and since the microtubules are relatively stable, then the granules move as a result of force generated between themselves and the microtubules, which represent a fixed cytoplasmic framework. To support this, they have demonstrated an association between granules and microtubules on the basis of nearest-neighbour type analysis, although no actual connections between granules and tubules have been observed.

Transport along nerve axons   The transport of axoplasmic constituents from the cell bodies of neurones down axons was first clearly documented by Weiss and Hiscoe (1948). By means of their 'damming' experiments they showed a movement towards the ends of the axons at approximately 1 mm per day. Similar blocking experiments, either by crushing or ligaturing, have since been carried out and have shown, for example, an accumulation of mitochondria (Weiss and Pillai, 1965) and an intensive increase in enzymatic reactions at the side of the obstruction nearest the cell body (Kreutzberg, 1969) as well as a widening of the affected stretches.

In addition to the slow movement, a much faster movement has also been shown to occur along axons. Experiments involving the injection of labelled precursors near neuronal cell bodies which were then traced after uptake and incorporation showed a crest of labelled activity descending at a rate close to 400 mm per day. There is thus an axonal and intra-axonal flow outwards from the cell body of proteins, enzymes, catecholamines, neurosecretory material and certain organelles all of which are required for the maintenance and function of the whole neurone.

It has been shown that developing nerves and mature vertebrate axons and dendrites (Wuerker and Kirkpatrick, 1972) contain longitudinally oriented microtubules (neurotubules), and also neurofilaments and microfilaments (Section 2.3; Fig. 5.3). It appears that small nerve fibres contain many neurotubules with fewer

Fig. 5.3 Nerve axon. Transverse section through a myelinated axon seen in the electron microscope. The axon contains both microtubules (MT) and neurofilaments (NF). (Courtesy of Dr O. Behnke.)

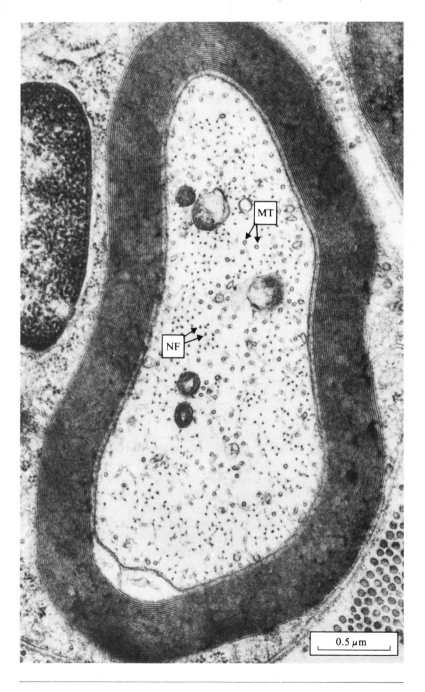

0.5 μm

neurofilaments, while the proportions of these fibrous proteins are reversed in larger nerve fibres, and in the latter the neurotubules are often arranged in clusters and groups, while in small nerve fibres they are usually evenly distributed.

The mechanism of fast and slow axoplasmic transport is not understood, and the respective roles of the neurotubules, neurofilaments and microfilaments are not clearly defined. The mass translatory movement of cytoplasm down axons at a rate of 1–3 mm day^{-1} has been related to growth in axoplasmic bulk (Weiss, 1961). On the other hand, experiments involving the injection of radioactive precursors into dorsal root ganglia followed by a period of downflow into the fibres and then a blockage by local freezing or ligation, to prevent further passage of labelled materials into the nerve fibre, have shown that once proteins and polysaccharides have gained entry to the axons, they continue to move at the usual fast rate (Ochs *et al.*, 1969). This demonstrates, of course, that there is transport down the fibre which is independent of any motive force exerted by the cell body.

Numerous studies have been carried out to examine the effects of antimitotic agents, such as colchicine, podophyllotoxin and vinblastine sulphate, all of which disrupt microtubules, on axoplasmic movements. These drugs have been shown to inhibit fast and occasionally slow axoplasmic flow, and their local application brings about a block in the same way as does a ligature (Kreutzberg, 1969; Paulson and McClure, 1975).

Ligation has therefore shown that the driving mechanism for fast axonal flow exists in the axon itself. Local innoxia of the nerve has further demonstrated that it depends on oxidative metabolism (Ochs, 1972) and the drug experiments have implicated the neurotubules. Further evidence for the participation of microtubules in axonal transport has derived from computer analysis of axon models (Smith *et al.*, 1975) which has revealed associations and physical linkages between the microtubules and the transported components.

Movement of ribosomes in insect ovaries during oogenesis The ovaries of hemipteran insects differ from those of other orders in that they are telotrophic. In such ovaries there is an anterior trophic region

---

Fig. 5.4 Telotrophic ovarioles of hemipteran insects. (*a*) A single ovariole of *Notonecta glauca* seen in polarised light. The nutritive tubes (arrows) appear strongly birefringent and can be seen to connect the developing oocytes to the trophic cells (TR). (*b*) Low power electron micrograph of a longitudinal section through a nutritive tube. The striated appearance of the tube is due to the enormous numbers of aligned microtubules which it contains. (*c*) Transverse section through a nutritive tube. The tubes are packed with microtubules and the ribosomes which are transported along them. ((*b*) From H. C. Macgregor and H. Stebbings (1970).)

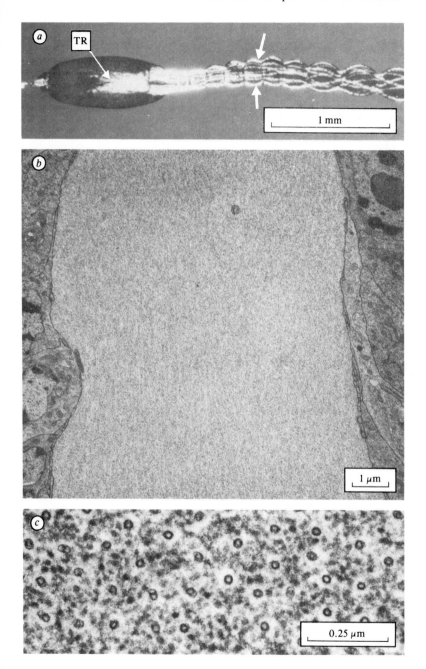

which connects to a chain of developing oocytes by way of so-called nutritive tubes (Fig. 5.4*a*), which may be up to 20*μ*m in diameter and 3 mm in length. Nutritive tubes are strongly birefringent when examined in polarised light and they contain an astonishing number of microtubules, of the order of 30,000, arranged longitudinally and parallel to the direction of transport (Macgregor and Stebbings, 1970; Figs. 5.4*b* and *c*).

Autoradiographic and ultrastructural studies have shown that in the ovaries of the water boatman, *Notonecta,* ribosomes pass along the nutritive tubes from the trophic cells to the oocytes at a rate of approximately 0.5 mm day^{-1} (Macgregor and Stebbings, 1970). Further experiments using a different species have suggested that there may, in addition, be a faster movement of a small fraction of RNA at 200 μm h^{-1} superimposed on this (Mays, 1972), possibly suggesting a biphasic transport reminiscent of axonal flow. It is interesting too, that in some hemipterans other components such as mitochondria also migrate down the nutritive tubes.

The role of the microtubules, if any, in the cytoplasmic transport is not yet clear, and the question as to whether they play a part in the generation of motive force, is unanswered. However, a comparative study of the nutritive tubes of different hemipterans (Hyams and Stebbings, 1977) has shown that there is considerable variation in the density of the microtubules in the nutritive tubes, and that this can to some extent be correlated with the size of components transported along the tubes of different species. These findings suggest that the microtubules in this system may act as a sieve and so determine what is transported and what is not. They also show that if the microtubules play an active role in the cytoplasmic transport, then this is not dependent on either their precise arrangement or their density.

Migration of nuclei in virus-induced syncytia   Many animal viruses cause animal cells to fuse and form multinucleate syncytia. Such fusion of hamster kidney fibroblasts has been carried out using simian para influenza virus and has been shown to result in a huge syncytium containing hundreds of nuclei (Holmes and Choppin, 1968). The nuclei do not remain scattered, but move through the cytoplasm to form tightly packed rows, and having done so, migrate towards the centre of the syncytium over a distance of up to 150 μm and at a rate of 1–2 μm min^{-1}. Holmes and Choppin showed that the nuclear migration was specific, although not all of the nuclei move at the same rate, and other cytoplasmic components are not transported.

Wide bands of weakly birefringent material lie between the rows of nuclei and these areas have been shown to contain bundles of microtubules and also 8 nm filaments. When cells infected with virus were incubated in the presence of colchicine they fused at the normal

132

rate, but their nuclei remained randomly scattered within the syncytium. Close examination showed that the colchicine had disrupted the microtubules but had no effect on the microfilaments.

Such experiments led to the conclusion that the microtubules were essential for the migration of the nuclei but did not determine whether they provided the motive force for such movements. The rows of nuclei, together with microtubules, are relatively free of other cytoplasmic components suggesting an association between the microtubules and the nuclei. However, no physical connections were seen by electron microscopy and the fact that the nuclei could sometimes be observed to roll end over end during migration would argue against an actual attachment.

Movement within suctorian tentacles Suctorians are sessile ciliates which are predatory or parasitic on other free swimming ciliates. They catch prey by means of fine stiff tentacles (Fig. 5.5a) and the contents of the prey pass along the tentacle into the body of the suctorian. As their name suggests, it has long been thought that the transfer of cytoplasm from prey to predator was accomplished by suction, and a variety of theories were advanced to explain how this was created. Kitching (1952) suggested, for example, that expansion of the suctorian body surface, coupled with a supposed resistance to inward collapse, might provide the suction for feeding and explained the wrinkling of the surface as being a local collapse which may occur when the uptake of food material from the prey fails to keep pace with expansion.

More recently the feeding and tentacle structure of a number of suctorians have been the subjects of close study. One such is *Tokophrya*, a free living fresh water organism which feeds on other ciliates, notably *Tetrahymena*. Each cell generates 10–60 tentacles depending on age and these are between 20–50 μm long, but less than 1 μm wide with a knob of approximately 2 μm diameter at their distal ends. Once captured by the tentacles of *Tokophrya*, the *Tetrahymena* appears to be paralysed in a few seconds. The process has been studied in detail by Rudzinska (1965) who reported that after attachment the tentacles broadened and shortened and that if one examines the tentacles with dark-field illumination one can initially observe a rapid centrifugal flow at the periphery of the tentacle which is then replaced by a centripetal stream of granules from the prey to the predator.

Closer observation in the electron microscope (Rudzinska, 1970) has shown that except for the distal part of the knob, the whole of the tentacle is covered by a pellicle and a plasma membrane. Following attachment, the tip of the tentacular knob contacts the pellicle and plasma membrane of the prey which break down, allowing it to make contact with the cytoplasm of the prey. The knob membrane then

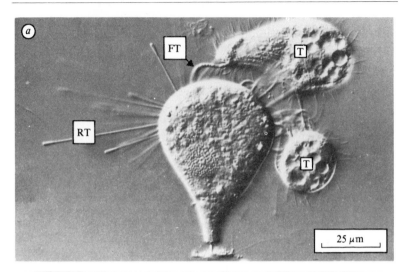

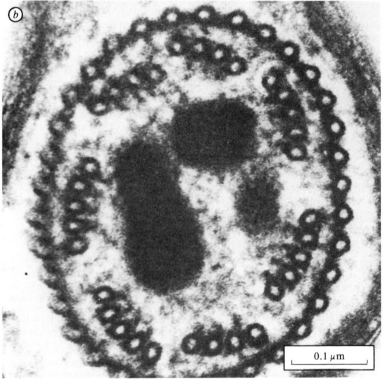

Fig. 5.5 Suctorian ciliates. (*a*) Nomarski interference contrast micrograph of *Tokophrya* feeding on two *Tetrahymena* (T). Feeding tentacles (FT) and resting tentacles (RT) can be clearly seen. (*b*) Transverse section showing the precisely ordered arrays of microtubules within the end of a resting tentacle. (From J. B. Tucker (1974).)

invaginates to such an extent that it extends throughout the whole of the tentacle, thus forming the inner of two concentric tubes (Fig. 5.6). Beyond the proximal end of the tentacle, within the cell body of the suctorian, the membrane balloons out and pinches off forming a food vacuole. Hence by invagination and the subsequent formation of food

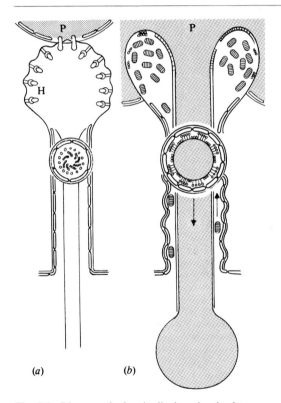

(*a*)   (*b*)

Fig. 5.6 Diagram of a longitudinal section (and transverse section inset) through a suctorian tentacle in resting (*a*) and feeding (*b*) states. Within and running the length of the tentacle is a cylinder of single microtubules and inside this an inner cylinder of microtubule ribbons. In (*a*) two haptocysts (H) have made contact with the prey (P). During feeding (*b*) the microtubules protrude into the knob at the end of the tentacle, and the membrane covering the knob together with the prey's cytoplasm (dotted) are transported through the tentacle. (From C. F. Bardele, *Symp. Soc. Exp. Biol.*, **28**, 191 (1974).)

vacuoles suctorians feed in a manner similar to many other protozoans.

In initial observations of the morphology of the tentacles Rudzinska (1965) observed a series of 'hollow fibrils' of 23 nm regularly grouped into seven bundles of seven fibrils running longitudinally and arranged in a fashion which encircled the lumen of the tentacles. She also noted that during feeding the configuration of the fibrils, which lay between the two concentric tubes, changed, suggesting that the tubular fibrils in the tentacles provide them with contractile elements which are perhaps responsible for the broadening of the inside of the tentacle at the start of feeding. In addition, and departing somewhat from the suction theory of suctorian movement, she proposed that the fibrils represented a structural basis for microwaves of contraction, which in passing down the tentacle could account for movement along its length.

It has now become increasingly clear that neither a pressure gradient hypothesis nor one which envisages a peristaltic action of elements in the tentacle can explain the observed feeding movements, particularly the upward movement of vesicles at the periphery of the tentacles. Consequently it seems more likely that the elements responsible for the propulsion of cytoplasm down the tentacle are located within the tentacles themselves and attention has therefore turned to the possible role of the microtubules in this system.

Based on observations on *Dendrocometes,* Bardele (1972) has proposed a 'grasp and swallow' mechanism to account for food ingestion in which it is suggested that a sliding back and forth of the inner cylinder of microtubule ribbons is responsible.

More recently, Tucker (1974) has re-examined resting and feeding tentacles of *Tokophrya* in detail, paying particular attention to the arrangement of and links between the microtubules at these different stages. He has discovered arms which project from the luminal surface of most of the row tubules throughout their length (Fig. 5.5*b*), and describes how on feeding the row microtubules in the tip of the knob bend outwards and apart so that the arm bearing surfaces of the tubules are positioned close to the invaginating cell membrane. In assuming that the membrane invagination moves downwards continuously throughout ingestion, rather than merely forming a stationary tube, and that contractile elements are located in the cytoplasm, Tucker proposes that the arms on the row tubules could either act as attachment points for these elements, or indeed represent the contractile elements themselves. In doing so, he points out, as did Bardele, that the arms have similar dimensions to the dynein arms of cilia and flagella.

5.1.2 Features of microtubule associated intracellular motility

From these examples, it can be seen that there are considerable variations in:

1. The number and arrangement of the microtubules associated with intracellular motility.
2. The nature and size of the components which are transported.
3. The manner and speed at which that transport takes place.
4. The selectivity of transport.

Number and arrangement of microtubules In some instances cytoplasmic movement may be associated with elaborate and distinct arrangements of cross-linked microtubules as illustrated in the cases of the heliozoan axopodium, where movement occurs outside, and the suctorian tentacle, where movement occurs within, a microtubule complex. More often, however, the microtubules are less ordered as is the case in nerve axons and insect nutritive tubes where there appears to be no immediately obvious relationship between the numbers and arrangement of microtubules and such factors as the size of the transport channel, the size or the amount of the components transported or the rate of movement.

What certainly seems significant is that in no instance where particles move alongside microtubules are they seen to make contact with the microtubule surface and indeed it is a feature of such systems that each microtubule appears surrounded by an electron-clear zone. The nature of this clear zone is unknown (see Chapter 2), and may well hold the key to an understanding of the mechanism of microtubule-associated transport. There have been reports of indistinct bridges extending across the clear zone between microtubules and particles which move along them (Smith, 1971) and Burton and Fernandez (1973) have described a network of lanthanum staining filamentous elements associated with the surfaces of axonal microtubules, but it is by no means established that they are ubiquitous to all situations where particles move along microtubule tracts.

Nature and size of components transported Perhaps the most striking feature of the association between microtubules and cytoplasmic movement is the considerable difference in the nature and sizes of the components transported in different systems. For example, proteins are transported along nerve axons, ribosomes of approximately 20 nm pass along nutritive tubes in telotrophic ovaries, membrane-bound melanin granules of 0.5 μm move along the processes of fish melanophores and in virus-induced syncytia, nuclei of 10 μm travel along tracts of microtubules. As can be seen from these few examples, there would seem to be a complete lack of any unifying feature between all the components transported and consequently it would appear likely that any fundamental mechanism of movement must be independent of properties of the moving particles.

Manner and speed of transport Where the particles which move within an intracellular system are large enough to be visualised by light

Table 5.1 Variation in the rate of intracellular movement associated with microtubules.

System	Rate of intracellular movement	Authors
Axonal flow (slow)	1 mm day^{-1}	Weiss and Hiscoe, 1948
Axonal flow (fast)	100–700 mm day^{-1}	See Dahlstrom, 1971
Movement of ribosomes in insect ovaries (slow)	0.5 mm day^{-1}	Macgregor and Stebbings, 1970
Movement of ribosomes in insect ovaries (fast)	200 μm h^{-1}	Mays, 1972
Melanin granules in melanophores (dispersion)	2 μm min^{-1}	
Melanin granules in melanophores (aggregation)	5 μm s^{-1}	Green, 1968
Migration of nuclei in syncytia	2.5 mm day^{-1}	Holmes and Choppin, 1968
Streaming in heliozoan axopodia	0.66 μm s^{-1}	Edds, 1975
Streaming down suctorian tentacles	0.98 μm s^{-1}	Hull, 1961

The second column also lists, aligned with rows: 42 μm h^{-1}; 4,167–29,169 μm h^{-1}; 21 μm h^{-1}; 200 μm h^{-1}; 120 μm h^{-1}; 18,000 μm h^{-1}; 105 μm h^{-1}; 2,376 μm h^{-1}; 3,528 μm h^{-1}.

microscopy, as for example in heliozoan axopodia and in fish melanophores, their movement can be observed directly. On the other hand where movement of large particles is very slow or where the movement can only be monitored by autoradiography, as in insect ovaries, then less is known about the actual manner of motility. A glance at Table 5.1 shows that there is an enormous variation in the rates of intracellular transport along microtubules ranging from 0.5 mm day^{-1} in insect ovaries to as much as 70 cm day^{-1} in some nerve axons. Such enormous differences in the rates of movement make it difficult to envisage a mechanism common to all the systems in question, and more likely perhaps that microtubules are involved in different phenomena in different cells.

Selectivity of transport   In many cases there appears to be a selectivity of components transported in different systems. For instance it is clear that during melanin granule migration in melanophores other organelles such as mitochondria do not move in conjunction with the migrating granules and the same is true where the nuclei migrate in virus-induced syncytia. A considerable degree of selectivity is also achieved by the transport system in telotrophic ovaries of, for example, the lesser water boatman *Corixa*. In the trophic region of the ovaries the nutritive cells continually break down and release all their contents into a central trophic core or reservoir, but despite this only free ribosomes are transported along the nutritive tubes to the developing oocytes even though the tubes are of an overall size which would accommodate much larger cell organelles. In the ovary of the cotton stainer, *Dysdercus*, mitochondria as well as ribosomes are transported along the nutritive tubes. Hyams and Stebbings (1977a) have demonstrated a correlation between the size of the particles transported and the density and arrangement of microtubules in the different species, but whether these parameters are solely responsible for the observed selectivity in this case remains to be seen.

5.1.3 Evidence for microtubules possessing a role in intracellular motility

Much of the further evidence for microtubules having a role in cytoplasmic movement is circumstantial. There have been innumerable experiments carried out which involve treating microtubule systems with antimitotic agents, such as colchicine, vinblastine sulphate and podophyllotoxin, or subjecting them to low temperature and high pressure prior to observing the effect of these treatments on cell function. In many cases it appears that intracellular motility is arrested by such treatments and does indeed coincide with microtubule disruption. Such experiments serve to indicate that microtubules are often essential for the movement to take place, although the experiments of Edds who substituted a glass rod for the microtubular axoneme of heliozoa have shown that this is not always the case. In situations where the disruption has shown the microtubules to be clearly indispensable, such experiments give no information as to whether the microtubules cause or merely facilitate the movement. They certainly do not show whether the microtubules are the units responsible for providing the motive force.

5.1.4 The molecular basis of microtubule-associated cell motility

A complete study of the molecular basis of cytoplasmic movement, and non-muscle motility in general, necessitates the isolation and subsequent characterisation of the system which exhibits the movement. The success of such an approach to our understanding of other forms of cell motility such as cilia and flagella has shown clearly that a microtubule-associated ATPase (dynein) is involved in producing motions in these organelles and probably also in the contractile axostyles of certain flagellates (see Chapter 3).

Most motile systems, however, are much less accessible than cilia and flagella and consequently the alternative approach of searching for suspected molecules, clearly linked with motility elsewhere, has been adopted.

Having eliminated the microtubular axoneme as responsible for the production of motility in heliozoan axopodia, Edds (1975b) turned his attention to examining the properties of the cytoplasm isolated from these organisms. He discovered that the cytoplasm was contractile, and that this contractility could be controlled in the same way as the myofibrils of vertebrate striated muscle, by manipulating the concentration of calcium ions and ATP. Furthermore, ultrastructural studies of isolated cytoplasm revealed thin filaments which bind HMM and are probably composed of actin, as well as thicker filaments which may conceivably be composed of myosin, inferring that a contractile system present in the cytoplasm may bring about the particle motions in axopodia.

Considerable amounts of actin, as well as tubulin, have also been found in growing nerve cells (Fine and Bray, 1971) and an actomyosin-like protein isolated from mammalian brain (Puszkin *et al.*, 1968). These might conceivably have a function in the motile processes of neurones and in an attempt to localise them, actin–HMM complexes have been seen oriented parallel to the long axes of mouse neuroblastoma axons (Chang and Goldman, 1973). In the case of nervous tissue as much attention has been paid to a different approach involving the study of proteins associated with extracted tubulin. In this regard, a protein with a molecular weight comparable to dynein has been reported in association with tubulin from brain tissue (Burns and Pollard, 1974), but little or no ATPase activity was detectable in preparations of this. In addition, similar microtubule-associated proteins (MAPs), occurring in association with brain tubulin, have been demonstrated as projections or arms attached to the neurotubules *in vitro* (see Chapter 2), and their possible function in motility cannot be excluded. The fact remains, however, that the relationship between these proteins and microtubules *in vivo* is unclear, and while they appear to be a consistent feature of brain tissue it remains to be seen whether they are found universally in association with tubulin in other systems.

What is really required is an elucidation of any microtubule-associated proteins *in vivo*. Hyams and Stebbings (1977b) have developed a technique for resolving the entire components of the transport system within the nutritive tubes of insect ovaries which, as has been outlined, is an intracellular motile system of extreme structural simplicity since the tubes appear to contain only microtubules and ribosomes in a cytoplasmic matrix. They discovered that with the benefit of polarised light, the nutritive tubes could be dissected intact from the ovaries, and harvested in large enough quantities to be subjected to SDS-polyacrylamide gel electrophoresis. In this way the entire transport system of the nutritive tubes was resolved into approximately 30 peptides, ranging in molecular weight between 23,000 and 340,000 daltons. The most prominent band proved, perhaps as expected, to be tubulin and represented 26% of the total protein and while some of the remaining bands could be attributed to ribosomal proteins, the origin of the remainder is not yet known. Of particular interest is the presence of a group of bands which migrated in the region of the MAPs, which as we have discussed, are seen to copurify with neurotubules *in vitro,* and may have a function in axonal transport.

5.1.5 Microtubules and mechanisms of motility

With the discovery of microtubules in an increasing number of systems exhibiting intracellular motility, and in the absence of conclusive data, theories have abounded as to their role in the observed movements. These can be divided into two categories – those in which it is proposed that microtubules have an *active* role in the generation of motive force, and others where they have a passive role, and merely define the direction of the movement. In some systems, notably in nervous tissue, there is the added complication in that neurotubules are not the only linear structures present, and more and more attention is being paid to filamentous structures which occur in association with microtubules, as is reflected in the following outlines of some of the different models for motility.

Microtubules actively involved in motility   In an attempt to explain fast axonal flow, Schmitt (1968) has suggested that there may be a matching of the bonding sites along the microtubules to those present on the surfaces of the transported vesicles (Fig. 5.7). He then considers the bonds between them to be made and broken as the vesicles jerk along the microtubules.

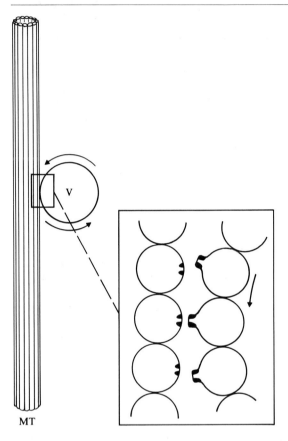

MT

Fig. 5.7 Diagram of the sliding vesicle model for the mechanism of fast specific transport of vesicles (V) by their interaction with microtubules (MT). (Redrawn from F. O. Schmitt, (1968).)

Other hypotheses are more closely based on the sliding filament theory of striated muscle (Ochs, 1971; Fig. 5.8). Here neurotubules or neurofilaments or both comprise the stationary member of the sliding filament pair, with a 'transport filament' synthesised in the somas and entering the axons to become the moving member of the pair of sliding filaments. To the transport filaments are bound somally synthesised small particulate substances, soluble proteins and polypeptides as well

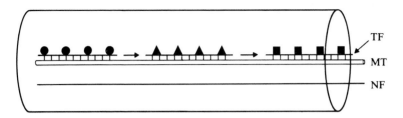

Fig. 5.8 Diagram summarising the transport filament model for fast axoplasmic transport in nerve. The model proposes that transport is achieved by the binding of components (●, ▲, ■) to transporting filaments (TF) which slide along the microtubules (MT) and/or neurofilaments (NF) using a cross-bridge mechanism analogous to that of striated muscle. (Redrawn from S. Ochs, (1971).)

as some free amino acids, all of which are carried down the axon on this common carrier at the same rate. Cross-bridges are assumed to perform a similar cycle of ratchet propulsions as has been proposed for the sliding filaments of muscle.

Considerable interest has centred on the possibility that arms or cross-bridges might develop the motive force for movement along microtubule tracts. In the case of teleost melanophores a close association between pigment granules and microtubules has been shown by nearest neighbour analysis (Murphy and Tilney, 1974) and actual projections, which could be analogous to cross-bridges (Smith, 1971), and lateral filamentous elements (Burton and Fernandez, 1973) have been seen in association with the surfaces of neurotubules. Distinct projections or arms have also been seen on the microtubules in suctorian tentacles. The nature of these arms and bridges is not known but is receiving attention, since arms with ATPase activity are clearly involved in producing motions in cilia and flagella, and could if present conceivably do so in other systems.

A passive role for microtubules in intracellular motility There are alternative hypotheses to explain microtubule-associated intracellular movement in which the microtubules form tracts which simply determine the direction of motility, but have no role in force generation.

For example, the movement down suctorian tentacles has been attributed to pressure gradients, the slow translatory movement of cytoplasm along nerve axons to growth in axoplasmic bulk (Weiss, 1961) and the migration of melanin granules in melanophores attributed to an electrophoretic effect (Kinosita, 1963).

The microtubules in axopodia clearly act solely as structural components, as we have already discussed, and it is proposed in this case that contractility in the cytoplasm, based on actin and myosin, may be responsible for motility. Similarly there is evidence for a microtubule-independent contractile system in fish melanophores (Schliwa and Bereiter-Hahn, 1975). Still further, the presence of actomyosin-like materials has led to models involving actin–myosin interactions, together with neurofilaments (Hoffman and Lasek, 1975) for explaining axonal flow.

5.2 Protoplasmic streaming and microfilaments

Apart from the shuttle streaming in myxomycete plasmodia, there are numerous examples of protoplasmic streaming in plant cells (Table 5.2), and indeed the phenomenon was first observed in these cells more than 200 years ago (Corti, 1774). The actual patterns of streaming exhibited are quite diverse, and have been classified into a number of categories (see Kamiya, 1959; Fig. 5.9). Least obvious is that described as 'agitation' where the motion is erratic and haphazard but nevertheless quite distinct from Brownian motion. Second, there is 'circulation' which is seen in cells having transvacuolar protoplasmic strands. Streaming of this sort is commonly found in cells of plant hairs, such as the stinging hairs of *Urtica* and the staminal hairs of *Tradescantia*. Here particles can be seen to stream within protoplasmic strands, and to even overtake each other and pass in opposite directions. The strands themselves show a continual alteration in pattern as they change in position and thickness, and branch, unite and shorten.

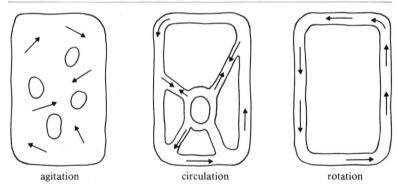

agitation	circulation	rotation

Fig. 5.9 Diagram showing different patterns of protoplasmic streaming exhibited by plant cells. (Redrawn from N. Kamiya, (1959).)

By contrast, 'rotational' streaming is the term used to describe the situation where the protoplasm around the periphery of the cell streams like a rotating belt. It differs from circulation in that there are no transvacuolar strands and the pattern of streaming remains constant. This type of streaming is seen in leaf cells of aquatic plants, such as *Elodea*, in root hair cells, and in pollen tubes, but is perhaps best known in some algal cells.

It is intriguing too, that transitions from one streaming type to another can occur within the same cell, as is illustrated by pollen grains as they form pollen tubes. In *Lilium*, for example, the grains initially show agitation, followed by circulation and then movement which can be regarded as rotational (Fig. 5.10; Iwanami, 1956).

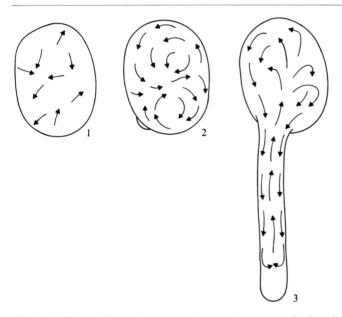

Fig. 5.10 Diagram illustrating patterns of protoplasmic streaming in pollen grains and young tubes of *Lilium*. As is indicated by the arrows, this ranges from agitation to circulation and also something akin to rotation. (After Y. Iwanami, (1956).)

One of the most impressive examples of rotational streaming and one which has received a great deal of attention, is that which occurs within the internodal cells of *Nitella*. These are relatively enormous elongated cells of between 2–5 cm in length. They possess a large central vacuole, as is often the case in plant cells showing cytoplasmic streaming, surrounded by a peripheral layer of cytoplasm. The

145

Table 5.2 Rate of protoplasmic streaming in various plant materials. Selected examples from Kamiya (1959).

Plant	Organ	Rate (μm s^{-1})	Author	Temperature (°C)
Caulerpa prolifera	'leaf'	2–3	Dostal (1929)	12–30
Nitella mucronata	internode	52	Umrath (1934)	20
Nitella flexilis	internode	78	Kamiya and Kuroda (1956)	28
Chara foetida	internode	42	Velten (1876a)	20
Chara braunii	internode	75	Hayashi (1952)	27
Elodea canadensis	leaf	10	Bushee (1908)	20
Elodea densa	leaf	6	Zurzycki (1951)	20
Tradescantia virginica	staminal hair	5.4	Kelso and Turner (1955)	24
Cucurbita maxima	petiole hair	4.3	Bushee (1908)	20
Allium cepa	inner epidermis	4	Jarosch (1956b)	
Avena sativa	coleoptile epidermis	10	Bottelier (1934)	21
Avena sativa	root hair	5.4	Bushee (1908)	20
Hydrocharis morsus ranae	root hair	8.1	Hofmeister (1867)	
Trianea bogotensis	root hair	9.5	Jurisic (1925)	18
Triticum aestivum	root hair	7.4	Doi (1950)	20
Oryza sativa	root hair	6.7	Doi (1950)	20
Hordeum vulgare	root hair	7.0	Doi (1950)	20
Zea mays	root hair	5.7	Doi (1950)	20
Raphanus sativus	root hair	4.8	Doi (1950)	20
Cucumis sativus	root hair	4.8	Doi (1950)	20
Lycopersicum esculentum	root hair	5.9	Doi (1950)	20
Spinacia oleracea	root hair	4.9	Doi (1950)	20
Lilium auratum	pollen tube	4.3	Iwanami (1953)	26
Oenothera lamarckiana	pollen tube	5.5	Iwanami (1953)	26
Vicia faba	pollen tube	2.9	Iwanami (1953)	20
Pisum sativum	pollen tube	2.3	Iwanami (1953)	24

cytoplasm consists of an outer stationary ectoplasm (gel) in which are found rows of spirally arranged chloroplasts and beneath this is a moving endoplasm (sol) which streams in a direction parallel to them (Fig. 5.11). In this case, the whole endoplasm circulates like a twisted

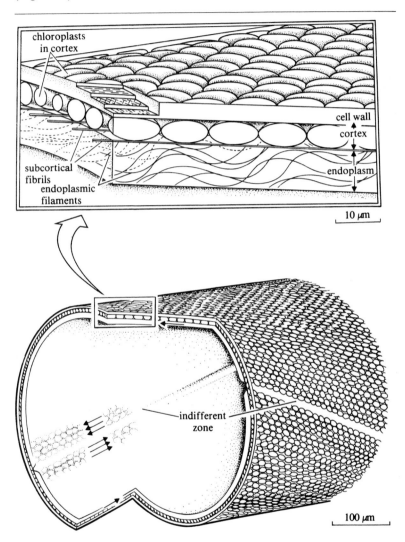

Fig. 5.11 Diagram of the cortical region of a *Nitella* cell showing the positioning of the endoplasmic filaments with respect to the cortex, the subcortical fibrils and the endoplasm. The lower diagram locates the upper one relative to the whole cell. (From N. S. Allen, (1974).)

belt with many particles including nuclei being carried along in the stream which moves at rates of up to $100 \, \mu m \, s^{-1}$, and is unidirectional.

Several lines of evidence indicate that the generation of force for movement is localised at the interface between the flowing endoplasm and the stationary cortical gel. For instance, while the entire endoplasm streams as a cohesive mass, the velocity decreases from the shear zone inwards towards the centre of the cell. Also, it appears that the movement is dependent on an intact cortical layer, since when this is damaged in some way, or removed by centrifugation, then normal movement is interfered with in that region.

These findings encouraged the search for the force generators in the interface region between the ectoplasm and the endoplasm. Employing a range of fixation techniques, Nagai and Rebhun (1966) observed subcortical fibrils running parallel to the rows of chloroplasts in the shear region, and discovered that these were composed of 50–100 microfilaments of 5 nm diameter. These, they proposed, were the components responsible for the force generation, since although microtubules were also present in the system their location and orientation made their involvement unlikely.

Subsequent to their discovery in *Nitella*, fibres composed of 5–7 nm

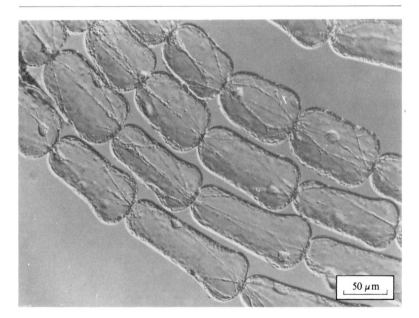

Fig. 5.12 Staminal hair cells of *Tradescantia*. Nomarski interference contrast micrograph showing the fine cytoplasmic strands along which streaming occurs.

microfilaments have also been observed in the peripheral cytoplasm of epidermal and parenchymal cells of a variety of higher plants (O'Brien and Thimmann, 1966; Parthasarathy and Muhlethaler, 1972), as well as in pollen tubes (Condeelis, 1974), where they are also associated with cytoplasmic streaming.

5.2.1 Action of cytochalasin B on protoplasmic streaming

It has been found that cytochalasin B reversibly inhibits the streaming in many plant cells, including *Nitella* (Williamson, 1972) and some higher plants. The staminal hair cells of *Tradescantia* (Fig. 5.12), for example, show streaming along fine tracts and streaming is arrested after one hour in 10 μg cm^{-3} cytochalasin B, but is restored when the drug is removed (see Fig. 5.13). Colchicine, on the other hand, has no effect on the streaming, even at quite high concentrations.

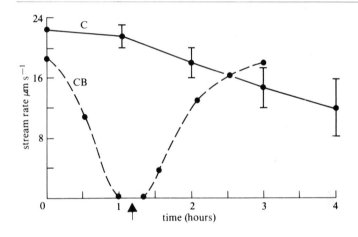

Fig. 5.13 Graph showing the effect of cytochalasin B (10 μg cm^{-3}) on the rate of streaming in staminal hair cells of *Tradescantia*. Such treatment (CB) arrests streaming within 1 h, while on removal of the drug (arrow) the streaming rate reverts to a level comparable to that of the control sample (C).

5.2.2 Molecular basis and mechanisms for cytoplasmic streaming

It has now been shown that the filaments associated with protoplasmic streaming in pollen tubes (Condeelis, 1974) and *Nitella* (Palevitz *et al.*, 1974) exhibit a beaded double helical structure and bind HMM to give the typical arrowhead arrays diagnostic of actin filaments (Fig. 2.12). Furthermore, the polarity of the filaments is such that the arrowheads point opposite to the direction of the motion, i.e. the protoplasmic stream, and are thus arranged similarly to those in striated muscle.

The actual mechanism of cytoplasmic streaming is unclear, but a number of hypotheses have been advanced. Light microscope studies of cytoplasmic droplets from algal cells have shown the presence of motile fibrils (Kuroda, 1964) and electron microscopy of the droplets has shown that they contain microfilaments which are believed to represent the motile fibrils. Undulating cytoplasmic fibrils have also been observed in living *Nitella* cells by Kamitsubo (1972) who developed a 'window technique' in which the overlying chloroplasts were removed using a beam of white light.

How does the movement of actin filaments produce the cytoplasmic streaming? Jarosch (1964) has proposed a screw-mechanical theory with torsional movements of the microfilament bundles propelling the cytoplasmic matrix, while Allen (1974) has noted that particles carried along in the stream exhibited 'serpentine' patterns and using refined optics observed that filaments, which in *Nitella* extend from the subcortical fibres, generated waves of bending similar to those generated by sperm tails (Fig. 5.11).

What does seem likely is that the filamentous movement, be it in the form of waves or torsion or whatever, may depend on an actin–myosin interaction, although no myosin filaments have yet been found in these systems.

References

ALLEN, N. S. (1974) Endoplasmic filaments generate the motive force for rotational streaming in *Nitella, J. Cell Biol.*, **63**, 270–87.

BARDELE, C. F. (1972) A microtubule model for ingestion and transport in the suctorian tentacle, *Z. Zellforsch Mikrosk. Anat.*, **126**, 116–34.

BURNS, R. G. and POLLARD, T. D. (1974) A dynein-like protein from brain, *FEBS (Fed. Eur. Biochem. Soc.) Lett.*, **40**, 274–80.

BURTON, P. R. and FERNANDEZ, H. L. (1973) Delineation by lanthanum staining of filamentous elements associated with the surfaces of axonal microtubules, *J. Cell Sci.*, **12**, 567–83.

CHANG, C-M. and GOLDMAN, R. D. (1973) The localization of actin-like fibres in cultured neuroblastoma cells as revealed by heavy meromyosin binding, *J. Cell Biol.*, **57**, 867–74.

CONDEELIS, J. S. (1974) The identification of F-actin in the pollen tube and protoplast of *Amaryllis belladonna, Exp. Cell Res.*, **88**, 435–9.

CORTI, B. (1774) Osservazioni microscopiche sulla tremella e sulla circolazione del fluido in un pianta acquajuola. Lucca.

DAHLSTRÖM, A. (1971) Axoplasmic transport (with particular respect to adrenergic neurons), *Phil. Trans. Roy. Soc. Lond. B*, **261**, 325–58.

EDDS, K. T. (1975a) Motility in *Echinosphaerium nucleofilum* I. An analysis of particle motions in the axopodia and a direct test of the involvement of the axoneme, *J. Cell Biol.*, **66**, 145–55.

EDDS, K. T. (1975b) Motility in *Echinosphaerium nucleofilum* II. Cytoplasmic contractility and its molecular basis, *J. Cell Biol.*, **66**, 156–64.

FINE, R. E. and BRAY, D. (1971) Actin in growing nerve cells, *Nature, New Biol.*, **234**, 115–8.

References

GREEN, L. (1968) Mechanism of movements of granules in melanocytes of *Fundulus heteroclitus, Proc. Natl. Acad. Sci.,* **59,** 1179.

HOFFMAN, P. N. and LASEK, R. J. (1975) The slow component of axonal transport. Identification of major structural polypeptides of the axon and their geniality among mammalian neurons, *J. Cell Biol.,* **66,** 351–66.

HOLMES, K. V. and CHOPPIN, P. W. (1968) On the role of microtubules in movement and alignment of nuclei in virus-induced syncytia, *J. Cell Biol.,* **39,** 526–43.

HULL, R. W. (1961) Studies on suctorian protozoa: The mechanism of ingestion of prey cytoplasm, *J. Protozool.,* **8,** 351–9.

HYAMS, J. S. and STEBBINGS, H. (1977a) The distribution and function of microtubules in nutritive tubes, *Tissue and Cell,* **9,** 539–47.

HYAMS, J. S. and STEBBINGS, H. (1977b) The isolation and characterisation of a cytoplasmic microtubule transport system, *J. Cell Biol.,* **75,** 271a.

IWANAMI, Y. (1956) Protoplasmic movement in pollen grains and tubes, *Phytomorphology,* **6,** 288–95.

JAROSCH, R. (1964) Screw mechanical basis of protoplasmic movement, in *Primitive Motile Systems in Cell Biology,* pp. 599–622, ed R. D. Allen and N. Kamiya. Academic Press, N.Y. and London.

KAMITSUBO, E. (1972) A 'window technique' for detailed observation of characean cytoplasmic streaming, *Exp. Cell Res.,* **74,** 613–6.

KAMIYA, N. (1959) Protoplasmic streaming, *Plasmatologia,* **8,** 1–199.

KINOSITA, H. (1963) Electrophoretic theory of pigment migration within fish melanophores, *Ann. N.Y. Acad. Sci.,* **100,** 992–1004.

KITCHING, J. A. (1952) Observations on the mechanism of feeding in the suctorian *Podophrya, J. Exp. Biol.,* **29,** 255–66.

KITCHING, J. A. (1964) In *Primitive Motile Systems in Cell Biology,* p. 445, eds R. D. Allen and N. Kamiya. Academic Press, N.Y.

KREUTZBERG, F. W. (1969) Neuronal dynamics and axonal flow, IV. Blockage of intra-axonal enzyme transport by colchicine, *Proc. Natl. Acad. Sci.,* **62,** 722–8.

KURODA, K. (1964) The behaviour of naked cytoplasmic drops isolated from plant cells, in *Primitive Motile Systems in Cell Biology,* pp. 31–41, eds R. D. Allen and N. Kamiya. Academic Press, N.Y. and London.

MACDONALD, A. C. and KITCHING, J. A. (1967) Axopodial filaments of Heliozoa, *Nature,* **215,** 99–100.

MACGREGOR, H. C. and STEBBINGS, H. (1970) A massive system of microtubules associated with cytoplasmic movement in telotrophic ovarioles, *J. Cell Sci.,* **6,** 431–49.

MAYS, V. (1972) Stofftransport im ovar von *Pyrrhocoris apterus* L., *Z. Zellforsch,* **123,** 395–410.

McKINNON, D. L. (1909) The optical properties of the contractile elements in Heliozoa, *J. Physiol.,* **38,** 254–8.

MURPHY, D. B. and TILNEY, L. G. (1974) The role of microtubules in the movement of pigment granules in teleost melanophores, *J. Cell Biol.,* **61,** 757–79.

NAGAI, R. and REBHUN, L. I. (1966) Cytoplasmic microfilaments in streaming *Nitella* cells, *J. Ultrastruct. Res.,* **14,** 571–89.

O'BRIEN, T. P. and THIMMANN, U. V. (1966) Intracellular fibres in oat coleoptile cells and their possible significance in cytoplasmic streaming, *Proc. Natl. Acad. Sci. USA,* **56,** 888–94.

OCHS, S. (1971) Characteristics and a model for fast axoplasmic transport in nerve, *J. Neurobiology,* **2,** 331–45.

OCHS, S. (1972) Fast transport of materials in mammalian nerve fibres. A fast transport mechanism which depends on oxidative metabolism, *Science,* **176,** 252–60.

OCHS, S., SABRI, M. I. and JOHNSON, J. (1969) Fast transport system of materials in mammalian nerve fibres, *Science,* **163,** 686–7.

Movement within cells

PALEVITZ, B. A., ASH, J. F. and HEPLER (1974) Actin in the green alga, *Nitella, Proc. Nat. Acad. Sci. USA,* **71,** 363–6.

PARTHASARATHY, M. V. and MUHLETHALER, K. (1972) Cytoplasmic microfilaments in plant cells, *J. Ultrastruct. Res.,* **38,** 46–62.

PAULSON, J. C. and McCLURE, W. O. (1975) Inhibition of axoplasmic transport by colchicine, podophyllotoxin and vinblastine: An effect on microtubules, *Ann. N.Y. Acad. Sci.,* **253,** 517–28.

PORTER, K. R. (1973) Microtubules in intracellular locomotion, in *Locomotion of Tissue Cells.* Ciba Foundation Symp. 149–69.

PUSZKIN, S., BERL, S., PUSZKIN, E. and CLARKE, D. D. (1968) Actomyosin-like protein isolated from mammalian brain, *Science,* **161,** 170–1.

ROSKIN, G. (1925) Über die axopodien der Heliozoa und die greiftentakeln der Ephelotidae, *Arch. Protistenk,* **52,** 207–16.

RUDZINSKA, M. A. (1965) The fine structure and function of the tentacle in *Tokophrya infusionum, J. Cell Biol.,* **25,** 459–77.

RUDZINSKA, M. A. (1970) The mechanism of food intake in *Tokophrya infusionum* and ultrastructural changes in food vacuoles during digestion, *J. Protozool.,* **17,** 626–41.

SCHLIWA, M. and BEREITER-HAHN, J. (1975) Pigment granules in fish melanophores: morphological and physiological studies. V. Evidence for a microtubule-independent contractile system, *Cell Tiss. Res.,* **158,** 61–73.

SCHMITT, F. O. (1968) Fibrous proteins – neuronal organelles, *Proc. Natl. Acad. Sci.,* **60,** 1092–101.

SMITH, D. S. (1971) On the significance of cross-bridges between microtubules and synaptic vesicles, *Phil. Trans. R. Soc. Ser. B,* **261,** 395–405.

SMITH, D. S., JÄRLFORS, V. and CAMERON, B. F. (1975) Morphological evidence for the participation of microtubules in axonal transport, *Ann. N.Y. Acad. Sci.,* **253,** 472–506.

TILNEY, L. G. and PORTER, K. R. (1965) Studies of the microtubules in Heliozoa. 1. The fine structure of *Actinosphaerium nucleofilum* (Barrett), with particular reference to the axial rod structure, *Protoplasma,* **60,** 317–44.

TUCKER, J. B. (1974) Microtubule arms and cytoplasmic streaming and microtubule bending and stretching of intertubule links in the feeding tentacle of the suctorian ciliate Tokophrya, *J. Cell Biol.,* **62,** 424–37.

WEISS, P. (1961) In *Regional Neurochemistry,* pp. 220–42, eds S. S. Kety and J. Elkes. Pergamon Press, London.

WEISS, P. and HISCOE, A. B. (1948) Experiments on the mechanism of nerve growth, *J. Exp. Zool.,* **107,** 315–95.

WEISS, P. and PILLAI, A. (1965) Convection and fate of mitochondria in nerve fibres: axonal flow as vehicle, *Proc. Natl. Acad. Sci.,* **54,** 48–56.

WILLIAMSON, R. E. (1972) A light-microscope study of the action of cytochalasin B on the cells and isolated cytoplasm of the Characeae, *J. Cell Sci.,* **10,** 811–9.

WUERKER, R. B. and KIRKPATRICK, J. B. (1972) Neuronal microtubules, neurofilaments and microfilaments, *Int. Rev. Cytol.,* **33,** 45–75.

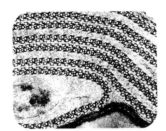

Chapter 6

Mitosis and cytokinesis

Cell division is a brief, albeit complex, period of the cell cycle in which the nuclear and cytoplasmic components of a single cell are distributed equally to two daughter cells. Division can be regarded as the cytologically visible reorganisation of components duplicated during the preceding *interphase*, that is, the relatively long period of the cell cycle during which most of its growth and synthesis takes place. Cell division proceeds by two distinct yet coordinated and overlapping events. In the first, a process known as *mitosis,* the *chromosomes* become sorted into two identical sets. In the second, *cytokinesis* or *cell cleavage,* the cytoplasm of the parent cell is divided into two packages which enclose the daughter nuclei. Although both are integral parts of continuous sequence of morphological changes which characterise cell division, mitosis and cytokinesis can be considered as two separate and unique phenomena. Cells may complete several cycles of mitosis without undergoing cleavage (and hence become multinucleate) and experimentally deformed cells will cleave without having previously passed through mitosis.

6.1 Mitosis

The faithful perpetuation of the genetic information of the cell through successive generations is a central and universal problem of modern biology. The cytologist observes only the final events of this complex saga, the packaging of the duplicated DNA into visible chromosomes and the distribution of the latter among the newly formed nuclei. Although the motions of the chromosomes through mitosis are complex, the task of describing their behaviour in general terms is fairly straightforward and usually done by reference to four, fairly arbitrarily defined, stages. The chromosomes appear at the beginning of *prophase* as fine threads which commence a sequence of coiling and condensation. Each chromosome can be seen at this stage to be composed of two identical copies, the *sister chromatids,* which exhibit an intimate lengthwise association. At some point along the length of the chromatids a primary constriction known as a *kinetochore* or *centromere* is also visible. Towards the completion of condensation the nuclear envelope disintegrates and the chromosomes become organised upon a bipolar framework of microtubules known as the *mitotic spindle*. Each chromatid at this point is directed towards one or other of the two spindle poles. As the cell enters *metaphase,* the chromosomes become aligned about the equator of the spindle where they await the detachment and separation of the chromatids during *anaphase.* In the final stage of mitosis, *telophase,* a reversal of the sequence of events observed during prophase, namely, the uncoiling of the chromatids and the re-establishment of the nuclear envelope, completes the formation of the two daughter nuclei. This sequence of chromosomal activity is illustrated in Figs. 6.1*a*—*h* and 6.2.

Despite a wealth of cytological descriptions of mitosis in an almost infinite variety of cells, the mechanism by which the chromosomes are moved to the poles of the spindle remains largely unknown. Quite understandably, most attention has been directed towards the spindle microtubules since, as we have seen previously, the role of microtubules in other motile phenomena is well established and since treatments known to disrupt microtubules generally result in a cessation of chromosome movement.

Why should such a ubiquitous cellular event as mitosis be so poorly understood when many quite obscure examples of cell motility are now reasonably well defined? First, unlike the contraction of muscle or the beating of cilia and flagella, mitosis is confined to only a brief period of the cell cycle. Hence, in contrast to the sarcomere or the axoneme, the mitotic spindle is a transient cellular structure which is immediately dismantled once the chromosomes have completed their tortuous journey. This fact alone has greatly hindered biochemical studies of mitosis which have lagged far behind the classical cytological descriptions of chromosome behaviour. Spindles may be isolated but have not yet been shown to support normal chromosome movements, possibly implying that essential components are lost during their separation from the cell. Despite this, analysis of isolated spindles by SDS–polyacrylamide gel electrophoresis has revealed a complexity which has effectively prevented the identification of their structural and enzymatic components. Attempts to investigate the movement of chromosomes in cell-free systems will in any event undoubtedly prove to be a far less tractable problem than has been found to be the case for either muscle or cilia and flagella since movement in these latter cases is cyclic and can be followed over long periods of time while mitosis occurs only once in the lifetime of most cells.

The second obstacle encountered by the student of mitosis is an almost unbelievable evolutionary diversity. The spindle may be composed of less than 50 microtubules as in the case of the yeast, *Saccharomyces*, or several thousand in the plant *Haemanthus*. The poles of the spindle, the foci into which the microtubules insert, are organised around a pair of centrioles in most animal cells but these are replaced by densely-staining plaque-like structures in many fungi while in plant cells there are no discernible structures at the spindle poles at all (Luykx, 1970). In many fungi and protozoa the spindle forms within the nucleus and the nuclear envelope remains intact throughout mitosis. This situation is often referred to as a *closed* mitosis. In the cells of all vertebrates and higher plants on the other hand, the spindle forms in the cytoplasm and the nuclear envelope breaks down during prophase. This is the so-called *open* mitosis shown in Fig. 6.2.

In this chapter we shall make no attempt to provide a comprehensive review of the literature on mitosis. Detailed coverage of this topic is already to be found in several excellent publications listed at the end of the chapter. Rather we shall concentrate on fairly recent evidence concerning the identification of the components of the spindle and the introduction of novel systems which may shed light on the nature of the motor which is used to drive the chromosomes.

6.1.1 Structure of the mitotic spindle

Bearing in mind the variation which is seen in the mitotic apparatus among different types of cell, it is impossible to select a single example which could be said in any way to be typical. We shall however focus our attention on the spindle of mammalian cells since they may be considered, in evolutionary terms, to be the most advanced and, thanks largely to the diligent studies of McIntosh and his colleagues (McIntosh and Landis, 1971; McIntosh *et al*., 1975a, b), their structure is reasonably well established (Fig. 6.3).

Spindle formation commences in the cytoplasm concomitantly with the appearance of the prophase chromosomes in the nucleus (Fig. 6.2). Microtubules are seen to emanate from a pair of centrioles which had replicated during the previous interphase forming star-like arrays or *asters*. The centrioles move towards their eventual positions at the opposite poles of the nucleus, possibly pushed apart by the growth and interdigitation of their respective microtubules. As prophase ends, the

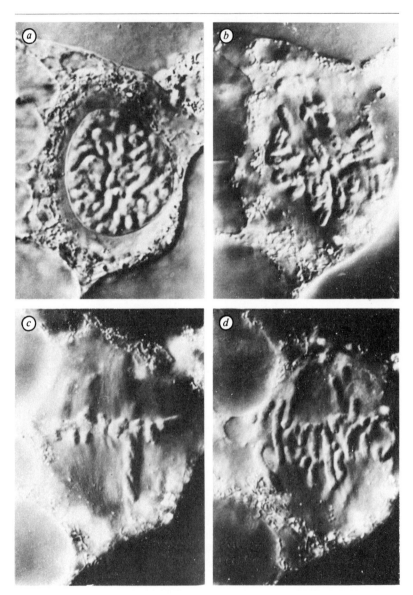

Fig. 6.1 Mitosis in the endosperm of *Haemanthus* as seen by Nomarski interference light microscopy. (*a*) Late *prophase*; the chromosomes are visible but the nuclear envelope is intact. (*b*) Late *prophase*; the nuclear envelope has now broken down. (*c*) *Metaphase*; chromosomes are aligned along the equator. Spindle fibres extending from the chromosomes to the pole can be detected. (*d*) Early *anaphase*; chromosomes have begun to move towards the poles. (*e*)–(*f*) Middle and late *anaphase*; the spindle has

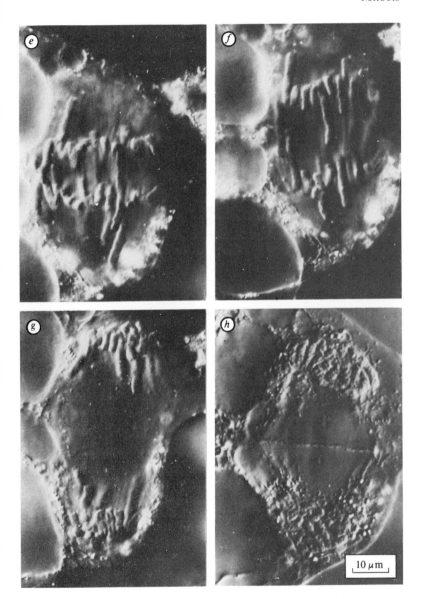

now increased in length. (*g*) *Telophase*; the chromosomes have completed their journey to the pole. (*h*) Late *telophase*; the chromosomes have become indistinct and the phragmoplast is starting to form across the equator. The time course of this sequence is about 2 h. (From A. S. Bajer, *Chromosoma*, **25**, 249 (1966).)

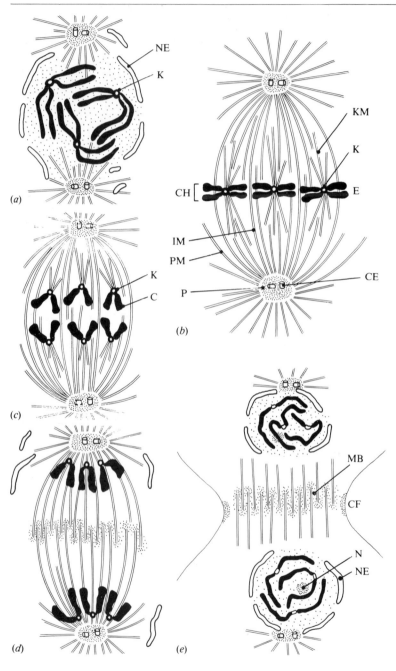

Fig. 6.2 Diagram depicting mitosis in a typical animal cell. (*a*) late prophase (*b*) metaphase (*c*) anaphase (*d*) telophase (*e*) late telophase and the start of cytokinesis. The sequence can be compared with that of a plant cell, *Haemanthus*, shown in Fig. 6.1. Abbreviations: NE, nuclear envelope; K, kinetochore; CH, metaphase chromosome; E, equator of spindle; C, chromatid; IM, interpolar microtubules; PM, polar microtubules; KM, kinetochore microtubules; P, pericentriolar material; CE, centriole; MB, midbody; CF, cleavage furrow; N, nucleolus. (Courtesy of Dr K. Roberts.)

nuclear envelope breaks down allowing the nucleoplasm and cytoplasm to mix and the microtubules to penetrate between the now fully condensed chromosomes (Figs. 6.1*b* and 6.2*b*). At the same time, microtubules assembled at the kinetochores of the chromosomes intermingle with those extending from the spindle poles (Fig. 6.3). The spindle at this point is completely formed, with the chromosomes aligned at the equator, the starting line for their subsequent anaphase movement, and the kinetochore of each sister chromatid pointing towards its ultimate destination at the spindle pole.

6.1.2 Distribution of spindle microtubules

By far the most extensive investigation of the organisation of spindle microtubules has involved a cultured cell line derived from the rat kangaroo and designated PtK$_1$. Such cells were fixed at various stages of division and serial sections taken perpendicular to the spindle axis. In this painstaking way, the number of microtubules at different levels through the spindle has been determined and an overall picture built up (McIntosh *et al.*, 1975a, b). A reconstruction of a PtK$_1$ metaphase spindle obtained in this manner is shown in Fig. 6.4.

From studies involving the *in vitro* polymerisation of microtubule protein (Section 2.2.6) it has been shown that both the chromosomal kinetochore and the amorphous material surrounding the centrioles at the spindle poles, are sites for the growth of spindle microtubules. The rat kangaroo has 11 chromosomes and section taken immediately adjacent to each centromere revealed approximately 34 microtubules emanating from each kinetochore. In other cells this number may vary from 1 in the fungus, *Thranstotheca*, to over 100 in *Haemanthus*. From Fig. 6.3 we can therefore immediately determine that there are many microtubules in each half of the PtK$_1$ spindle, and extending through the equator, which do not originate at the kinetochores. The number of microtubules at each pole however is low, such that even if none of the kinetochore microtubules extended all the way to the poles, the number of microtubules at the poles plus a set of kinetochore microtubules still does not add up to the total number counted in each half of the spindle. The spindle therefore must contain microtubules which neither begin nor end at a pole or centriole. This has in fact been confirmed by tracking individual microtubules through adjacent serial

159

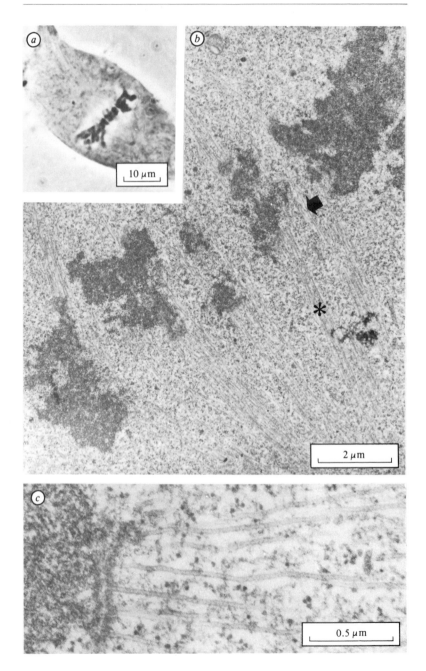

Fig. 6.3 Structure of the mitotic spindle of PtK₁. (*a*) Metaphase cell embedded in plastic prior to sectioning for electron microscopy. Spindle fibres extending from the chromosomes to two dark poles are evident. (*b*) Longitudinal section through the cell shown in (*a*). Bundles of microtubules are seen to extend either from the chromosomes to the poles (*) or between the chromosomes (arrow). (*c*) Kinetochore of a PtK₁ chromosome. These structures provide the site of growth and anchorage for the many microtubules which extend from them. ((*a*) and (*b*) from U-P. Roos, *Chromosoma,* **40,** 43 (1973); (*c*) is from U-P. Roos, *Chromosoma,* **41,** 195 (1973).)

sections which has identified lengths of microtubule as short as 0.2 μm. We can therefore regard the PtK₁ spindle as being composed of three families of microtubules, those which end at a pole (polar

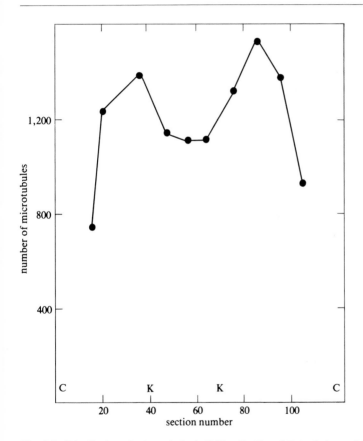

Fig. 6.4 Distribution of microtubules in PtK₁ cells. K and C mark the position of the kinetochores of each set of chromosomes and the centrioles of the spindle respectively. (Redrawn from McIntosh *et al.* (1975).)

microtubules), at a kinetochore (kinetochore microtubules) or with both ends free (free microtubules).

6.1.3 Actin in the spindle

Although microtubules are the only linear elements visible in the electron microscope, a considerable body of circumstantial evidence has accumulated to suggest the presence of an additional, unseen, fibrous system. Theoretical calculations have indicated that microtubules comprise as little as 10% of the mass of the isolated spindle and in fact the extraction of the microtubules causes no obvious change in the appearance of the spindle when examined by phase contrast light microscopy. Experiments in which individual chromosomal fibres were irradiated with a uv microbeam noted that even though the birefringence of the fibres was destroyed, the anaphase movement of the chromosome was unaffected. Conversely other treatments have been shown to slow down the movement of the chromosomes while having little effect on the birefringence of the spindle.

The first indication of the nature of this hypothesised second component of the spindle was provided by experiments in which both mitotic and meiotic spindles were glycerinated and treated with HMM (Behnke *et al.*, 1971). These quite clearly revealed the presence of microfilaments decorated with the characteristic arrowhead pattern. The obvious implication of this discovery, that microfilaments were an integral component of the spindle, not seen in the electron microscope because of problems of specimen preservation (Section 2.3.1), was far from generally accepted. Sceptics pointed to the fact that filaments were rarely seen in untreated material and could therefore be due either to the displacement of cytoplasmic microfilaments during glycerination or to the polymerisation of soluble actin by heavy meromyosin (Section 2.3.1).

This impasse remained until the introduction of techniques for the localisation of structural cellular proteins by means of fluorescent antibodies (Section 2.3.2). PtK$_1$ cells treated with antibody directed against muscle actin showed that fluorescence accumulated at the poles of the forming spindle but during metaphase could be detected as discrete fibres extending from each pole towards the chromosomes (Cande *et al.*, 1977). Probably a single fibre connected to each chromosome, the fibres apparently following the circular arcs of the kinetochore microtubules. As the chromosomes separated at anaphase, the fluorescent actin fibres were observed to shorten, although no fluorescence was detected in the *interzone*, that is the space between the separating sister chromatids.

Confirmatory evidence was forthcoming from experiments in which cells were similarly treated with antibody made against HMM which should also specifically react with microfilaments (Schloss *et al.*, 1977). Again fluorescent fibres extending from pole to chromosome were clearly visible (Fig. 6.5*a, b*) but again no fluorescence was seen in the interzone (Fig. 6.5*c*).

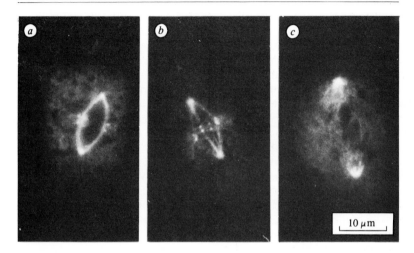

Fig. 6.5 Localisation of actin filaments in PtK₁ spindles by means of fluorescent HMM. (*a*), (*b*) Metaphase cells showing strongly fluorescent chromosome to pole fibres and kinetochores. (*c*) Anaphase cell showing short chromosome to pole fibres but no fluorescence in the interzone. (From J. A. Schloss, *et al.* (1977).)

The identification of actin in the spindle on its own might simply be taken to indicate that microfilaments were structural elements of the mitotic apparatus. (Although in Chapter 4 we described how actin alone might generate movement by its controlled polymerisation or redistribution, there is no evidence to suggest that force could be generated by its depolymerisation as would be required in this context.) The additional presence of myosin on the other hand would be far more convincing evidence that these muscle proteins were the motor which drives the chromosomes. Evidence to this point is as yet preliminary although in a very carefully controlled series of experiments, Fujiwara and Pollard (1976) followed the distribution of myosin antibodies in dividing human cells. During interphase and prophase the whole cytoplasm was strongly fluorescent. At metaphase and early anaphase however, fluorescence, although now much weaker, was concentrated in the spindle and in particular was seen to decorate fibres extending from the poles to the chromosomes, in fact similar to those seen with antibodies to either actin or HMM.

However, when the fluorescent antibody was passed through further purification steps no labelling was detected. Clearly the presence of myosin in the spindle is a very open question.

Many questions concerning the presence of muscle proteins in the spindle obviously remain to be answered. If microfilaments are really present in the spindle, do they insert into the kinetochore or some other point along the chromosome? How many microfilaments comprise the fibres seen by immunofluorescence? Do microfilaments extending between the chromosomes and the poles interact with the kinetochore microtubules? Is myosin really a component of the chromosomal fibres and if so how is it organised with respect to the microfilaments? Such problems will without doubt test the imagination of workers engaged upon investigations of the mechanism of chromosome movement for many years to come.

6.1.4 Mechanisms of mitosis

One aspect of mitosis about which there is fairly general agreement is that the force for chromosome movement is exerted largely at the kinetochore. When chromosomes are moved to the poles at anaphase, the kinetochores lead the way with the arms of the chromosome trailing behind. Micromanipulation studies have shown that although chromosomes may be swung around the pole region or stretched to several times their original length, the kinetochore to pole distance remains constant. Similarly, during anaphase, chromosomes are easily pushed closer to the pole but pulled away from it only with great difficulty. Chromosome fragments induced by X-rays or chemicals and which lack kinetochores do not undergo anaphase movements, neither do chromosomes in which the kinetochore has been destroyed by irradiation with uv light. These observations taken together show that the chromosomal fibre, consisting of a variable number of microtubules, firmly attaches the chromosome to the pole, and it is through the attachment that force is imparted to the chromosome.

Of the multitude of mechanisms of mitosis which have been proposed during the last decade, two types of model have received serious consideration from workers in the field, partly because they are backed by experimental observations. The first considers that movement is generated by the depolymerisation of the microtubules comprising the chromosomal fibre, the second by the interaction of these microtubules with microtubules extending from the poles or lying free within the spindle. As the evidence for the presence of microfilaments in the spindle becomes ever more compelling, no doubt the next ten years will see the emergence of models in which chromosomes are moved by actin–myosin interactions while microtubules serve as a structural framework upon which these muscle proteins are organised. Possibly the truth will be found to lie in a combination of all these possibilities but for now, since only the distribution of microtubules in the spindle is known with any certainty, we will consider how they alone might generate chromosome movement.

Attempts to understand mitosis in this way have concentrated almost exclusively on anaphase because this is by far the most dramatic period of chromosome movement and hence the easiest to monitor in the light microscope. Anaphase is usually considered in terms of two separate events on the basis of different sensitivity to various chemical treatments. The first is the movement of the chromosomes to the poles of the spindle, the second the elongation of the spindle to move the poles, and hence the chromosomes, further apart. In some cells the two events occur concurrently while in others they show a clear temporal separation. Quite obviously the first event involves the shortening of the microtubules connecting chromosome and pole while the second requires the elongation of the polar microtubules.

Depolymerisation of the chromosomal fibre   In Chapter 2 we considered briefly the concept that the spindle was a dynamic structure undergoing constant changes in equilibrium between polymerised microtubules and their subunits. This was based largely upon observations of living spindles in polarised light (Fig. 6.6), which revealed a conspicuous 'flickering' effect as if components were constantly being added at the kinetochores and removed at the poles. This interpretation was supported by the study of cytoplasmic particles introduced into the prometaphase spindle by micromanipulation. These were found to move towards the spindle poles at rates comparable to the anaphase movement of chromosomes, as if there was a continuous flow of material to the poles even before the chromosomes became aligned at the metaphase plate.

The dynamic nature of spindle microtubules has been interpreted by Inoué and Ritter (1975) as being of importance not only in the formation of the spindle but also in the movement of the chromosomes. Their evidence for this belief derives largely from studies of metaphase-arrested oocytes of the parchment worm, *Chaetopterus,* in which one pole of the spindle becomes attached via its aster to the cell cortex. When rapidly chilled to 4°C, spindle birefringence quickly fades away, due to the depolymerisation of the labile microtubules. When cooled gently, however, the kinetochore microtubules were seen to depolymerise slowly with the result that the chromosomes moved towards the pole anchored at the cell cortex. Similar results were obtained with low concentrations of colchicine, the milder the treatment the slower the rate of chromosome movement. When cells were restored to normal conditions, the spindle reformed and chromosomes returned to their position at the equator.

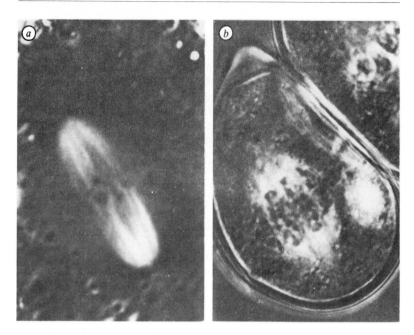

Fig. 6.6 Birefringence of spindle fibres. (*a*) Metaphase spindle of an animal cell, the oocyte of the parchment worm *Chaetopterus*. (*b*) Early anaphase in the plant, *Lilium*. Both reveal strongly birefringent chromosomal fibres when examined in polarised light. Only in the animal cell are astral fibres distinguished. These appear dark as they are perpendicular to the plane of the polariser. (Courtesy of Dr S. Inoué.)

A more rigorous examination of this phenomenon using high pressure to disrupt the microtubules was equally revealing (Salmon, 1975). Again, chromosome movements were shown to be proportional to the pressure applied (and hence to the shortening of the kinetochore microtubules), reaching a maximum of 17 μm min^{-1}, or two to three times the normal anaphase velocity, at 5,500 psi.

The correlation between the movement of chromosomes and shortening of the chromosomal fibre under these artificial conditions is supported by observations of natural fluctuations of birefringence during anaphase in both plant and animal cells (Fuseler, 1975). During anaphase, the birefringence of chromosomal fibres was observed to exhibit a gradual decay. The rate of decay was greatly increased at elevated temperatures, conditions which produced a corresponding increase in the rate of chromosome movement. In both the induced and natural systems therefore, chromosome movement has been shown to be directly proportional to the depolymerisation of the microtubules comprising the chromosomal fibre. Inoué and Ritter (1975) suggest that this depolymerisation actually drives the movement of chromosomes and have produced calculations which indicate that this interpretation is indeed possible. Other workers, however, are of the opinion that the shortening of the kinetochore microtubules merely governs the rate of movement generated by some other system.

The sliding microtubule model   Based on the sliding filament theory of muscle contraction (Chapter 1), the sliding microtubule model of chromosome movement (McIntosh *et al.*, 1969) arose in response to numerous observations of cross-bridges between the microtubules of the mitotic spindle. The model represented an enormous intellectual contribution to our understanding of mitosis, so much so that of the multitude of proposed mechanisms of chromosome movement it has received by far the most serious attention from workers in the field.

The model, which is summarised in Fig. 6.7, requires two basic assumptions. The first is that the bridges connecting spindle microtubules are mechanochemical enzymes, analogous to the side-arms of cilia and flagella or the cross-bridges of muscle and therefore capable of converting chemical energy stored in compounds such as ATP into mechanical work. The second assumption, now well supported by experimental observation, is that the spindle is composed of (at least) two families of microtubules with opposite polarity or direction. That is, one group which grows from the kinetochores to the poles and another which grows from the poles in the opposite direction. This is shown by the large arrowheads in Fig. 6.7, the smaller ones indicating the direction of force generated by the cross-bridges.

Bridges connecting microtubules of the same polarity will exert no net force as indicated by the crossed arrows in Fig. 6.7*a*, while those joining oppositely directed microtubules will, if not constrained, generate movement by sliding adjacent microtubules along one another. Metaphase in this scheme is regarded as a stable situation in which the sister chromatids remain attached and the forces exerted on each kinetochore are mutually opposed (Fig. 6.7*a*). Anaphase will begin with the disturbance of the metaphase equilibrium, possibly by the disruption of the chromatid links, which allows each kinetochore microtubule to slide polewards against one polar microtubule while dragging a second along with it (Fig. 6.7*b*, *c*). Since at the same time both kinetochore and polar microtubules are shortening by the removal of subunits at their polar termini, the net result is the displacement of the chromosomes to the poles (Fig. 6.7*b*, *c*). Sliding will cease when there is no longer any overlap between the two sets of polar microtubules (Fig. 6.7*c*). However, the elongation of the latter, possibly by the addition of subunits derived from the depolymerisation

167

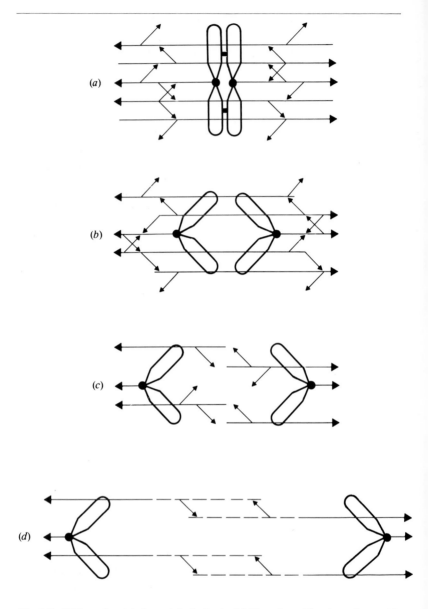

Fig. 6.7 Sliding microtubule model of mitosis: (*a*) Metaphase. The sister chromatids are linked together. Straight lines represent a minimal number of pole to pole or chromosome to pole microtubules. The large arrowheads indicate the polarity of the microtubules, the small ones the direction of force generated by hypothetical cross-bridges. (*b*), (*c*) Two stages of anaphase movement following disruption of the

connection between the chromatids. Movement of the chromosomes is accompanied by shortening of both groups of microtubules. (*d*) Elongation of the pole to pole microtubules (dashed lines) re-establishes a region of overlap. Further sliding results in the elongation of the spindle and hence separation of the poles. The essential features of the model are also described in the text. (Redrawn from R. B. Kicklaus (1971).)

of microtubules during the poleward journey of the chromosomes, will re-establish the zone of overlap and allow further sliding to mediate the separation of the spindle poles (Fig. 6.7*d*).

Is there any experimental evidence to support the sliding microtubule model? Dividing PtK$_1$ cells, gently lysed with detergent into a solution of microtubule protein to stabilise the fragile spindle together with either ATP or GTP will continue the anaphase separation of their chromosomes at rates which closely resemble those from living cells (Cande *et al.*, 1974; McIntosh *et al.*, 1975a). This *in vitro* chromosome movement can be stopped by manipulation of the ionic environment of the lysed cell and restarted by the addition of axonemal dynein, perhaps indicating that this enzyme is the chromosome 'motor'. Interestingly, the addition of molecules which would presumably inhibit movement generated by microfilaments, such as HMM or antibodies directed against either actin or myosin, failed to arrest chromosome motion.

In addition to such biochemical manipulations, the sliding microtubule model makes certain predictions which are testable by ultrastructural analysis of the anaphase spindle. First, microtubules in the interzone must be closely positioned such that cross-bridges can span the distance between them. Second, counts of microtubules through the interzone should reveal twice as many microtubules in the region of overlap as either side of it (Fig. 6.7*d*). Both of these predictions find support from experimental data. Observation, by polarised light microscopy, of living cells passing through anaphase reveals wispy birefringent fibres extending past the chromosomes and into the interzone. In the electron microscope these were found to be tightly bunched groups of microtubules. Towards the end of anaphase and into telophase these groups coalesce, eventually forming the midbody which persists for varying periods of time between the almost separated daughter cells (Fig. 6.2). Counts of microtubules in the anaphase interzone invariably revealed a distribution lower than the hypothesised 2:1 ratio, an observation widely quoted by antagonists of the model. However, sections through the midbody itself were found to be very close to the predicted values.

6.1.5 Mitosis in *Diatoma*

Some very interesting evidence which supports the hypothesis that microtubule sliding is involved at least in the elongation of the anaphase spindle has come from perhaps a rather unexpected source, namely the diatom, *Diatoma* (McDonald *et al.*, 1977). Contrary to the situation in mammalian cells where the microtubules do not form nice ordered patterns which would facilitate an analysis of their interactions, the spindle of this organism is a very regular structure. A bundle of approximately 100 parallel microtubules extends from the plaque-like structures at each spindle pole to the middle of the cell where the two groups interdigitate and form a region of overlap (Figs. 6.8 and 6.9). In addition to this *central spindle* a few additional microtubules radiate tangentially from the poles towards the diffuse chromatin. These may be equivalent to the kinetochore microtubules of mammalian and other cells.

The anaphase movement of the chromosomes to the poles involves no change in the length of the spindle which at this point measures about 5 μm (Fig. 6.8*a*, *b*). Once the chromosomes have reached the poles the central spindle elongates by about 2 μm, or approximately the original amount of overlap between the two groups of polar microtubules which now appears greatly reduced (Fig. 6.8*c*). Sections taken through the region of overlap as elongation takes place are equally revealing, showing a progressive increase in the staining intensity of the cytoplasm surrounding the microtubules, possibly as the result of some enzymatic activity (Fig. 6.9*a–d*). By far the simplest interpretation of these observations is that spindle elongation in *Diatoma* is the result of the sliding apart of two halves of the central spindle due to mechanochemical interactions between the microtubules. Quite clearly, further investigations of simple systems such as *Diatoma* where the spindle microtubules exhibit a well-ordered arrangement, may contribute enormously to our understanding of the mechanism or mechanisms of mitosis.

6.2 Cytokinesis

Before mitosis is complete, usually in late anaphase or early telophase, the dividing cell undergoes another series of morphological changes designed to apportion the cytoplasm of the parent cell, and hence such

Fig. 6.8 Anaphase spindle elongation in *Diatoma*. Longitudinal sections through spindles at (*a*) metaphase, (*b*) anaphase and (*c*) telophase. (*a*) The spindle can be seen to be composed of two groups of microtubules. One is a parallel bundle of microtubules which extends from each spindle pole (arrows) to the equator where the two groups interdigitate and form a region of overlap (O). The second is a number of microtubules which diverge from the poles at various angles (L) and extend towards the chromatin (C) which occupies the equatorial plane. (*b*) The chromatin has moved towards the poles with no change in the length of the spindle. (*c*) Once the chromatin has reached the poles the spindle elongates (note that the magnification of this figure is lower than in (*a*) and (*b*)) and the region of overlap decreases markedly. (From K. McDonald *et al.* (1977).)

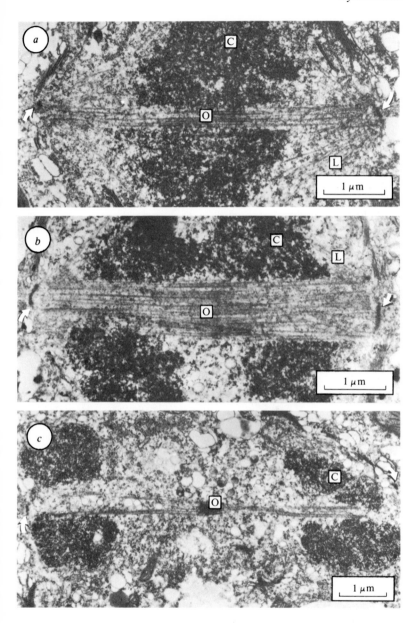

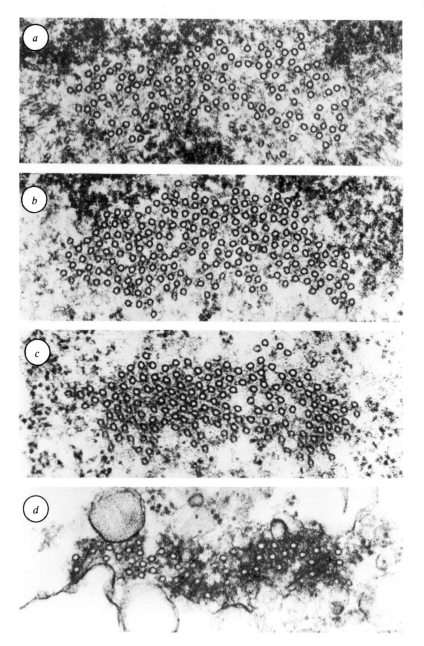

Fig. 6.9 Anaphase spindle elongation in *Diatoma*. Transverse sections through: (*a*) metaphase spindle outside the region of overlap, (*b*) the same spindle but within the region of overlap. Note that there are approximately twice the number of microtubules as in (*a*). (*c*) Anaphase spindle within the region of overlap. Compare the density of the cytoplasmic matrix surrounding the microtubules with that in (*b*). (*d*) Telophase spindle within the region of overlap. The intermicrotubule matrix is now densely stained. (From K. McDonald *et al.* (1977).)

organelles as ribosomes and mitochondria, more or less equally to the two daughter nuclei. This process is usually referred to as *cytokinesis*. In plant cells the division of the cytoplasm is achieved via the formation of a *phragmoplast*, a system of vesicles which become aligned across the middle of the cell, coalesce and eventually determine the formation of a new cell wall (Fig. 6.1*h*). In animal cells on the other hand, cytokinesis proceeds by a quite different mechanism, an invagination of the plasma membrane at the equator of the cell known as the *cleavage furrow*, gradually constricting the cell almost as if a drawstring were being tightly pulled about its middle (Fig. 6.10).

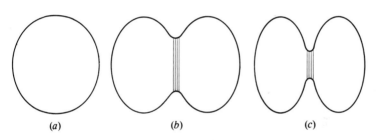

(*a*) (*b*) (*c*)

Fig. 6.10 Diagram depicting cytokinesis in an animal cell. A band of microfilaments, the contractile ring, constricts the cell at the equator, forming a cleavage furrow which eventually partitions the cell's cytoplasm into two more or less equal portions.

Examination in the electron microscope of the cytoplasm immediately beneath the cleavage furrow reveals a specialisation not seen elsewhere in the cell cortex. A system of some 5,000 circumferentially oriented filaments, each 5–7 nm in diameter and forming a band approximately 10–15 μm wide, is seen to lie immediately beneath the cell membrane and parallel to the plane of the cleavage furrow (Fig. 6.11). When exposed to HMM the filaments of the band reveal the arrowhead decoration characteristic of microfilaments (Perry *et al.*, 1971; Schroeder 1973). This information as to the nature of the band, together with its intimate association with the cleavage furrow, suggested that it was a likely candidate for the

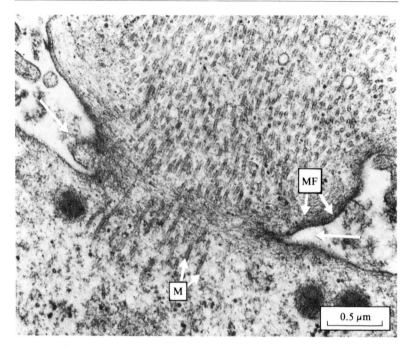

Fig. 6.11 Contractile ring of cleaving rat egg. A prominent system of microfilaments (MF) underlies the cleavage furrow (arrows) of this dividing cell. Microtubules (M) persisting from the mitotic spindle are compressed by the constriction about the middle of the cell. (From D. Szollosi, *J. Cell Biol.*, **44**, 192 (1970).)

force-generating element of cell cleavage and it was hence designated the *contractile ring*.

The contractile ring invariably forms about that region of the spindle previously occupied by the chromosomes at metaphase. Constriction in this region leads to the pulling together of the interzone spindle microtubules to form the midbody. Several lines of evidence, however, suggest that it is not the spindle which determines the positioning of the contractile ring but rather the asters which are apparently involved in the organisation of the cell surface. This influence is presumably indirect since compounds such as colchicine and D_2O which affect the formation of microtubules do not interfere with cleavage.

Like the mitotic spindle, the contractile ring is an ephemeral organelle which is formed extremely rapidly, probably in less than 10 minutes. Because of this rapid assembly we can only speculate as to whether the contractile ring is formed by the rapid polymerisation of a pre-existing pool of actin subunits (Section 2.4.3) or by the lateral aggregation of microfilaments already existing elsewhere in the cell cortex. The width and thickness of the contractile ring, and also the spacing of the individual microfilaments, remain constant throughout cleavage although the length of the contractile ring obviously shortens as the constriction about the middle of the cell decreases in diameter (Fig. 6.10). The volume of the ring is therefore evidently reduced as cleavage proceeds indicating that the microfilaments are being continually disassembled.

Although no thick (myosin) filaments are seen in the electron microscope the obvious inference of the presence of microfilaments within the contractile ring is that cleavage is generated by some sort of actin–myosin interaction. Schroeder (1975) has proposed probably the best model for this sort of mechanism which envisages that the microfilaments anchored to the cell membrane interact laterally by means of bipolar myosin molecules. More recently, evidence to support this hypothesis has appeared in the form of studies using fluorescent antibody against myosin which strongly decorates the cleavage furrow of human cells (Fujiwara and Pollard, 1976) and from the observation that the microinjection of myosin antibodies into starfish blastomeres completely inhibits cell cleavage (Mabuchi and Okhuno, 1977).

Suggestions for further reading and references

Further reading
BAJER, A. S. and MOLÈ-BAJER, J. (1972) Spindle dynamics and chromosome movement, *Int. Rev. Cytol.,* Supplement 3, 1–271.
KUBAI, D. F. (1975) The evolution of the mitotic spindle, *Int. Rev. Cytol.,* **43,** 167–227.
NICKLAS, R. B. (1971) Mytosis in *Advances in Cell Biology,* Vol. 2, pp. 225–97, eds D. M. Prescott, L. Goldstein and E. McConkey. Appleton-Century-Crofts, N.Y.

References
BEHNKE, O., FORER, A. and EMMERSEN, J. (1971) Actin in sperm tails and meiotic spindles, *Nature,* **234,** 408–10.
CANDE, W. Z., SNYDER, J., SMITH, D., SUMMERS, K. and McINTOSH, J. R. (1974) A functional mitotic spindle prepared from mammalian cells in culture. *Proc. Nat. Acad. Sci. USA,* **71,** 1559–63.
CANDE, W. Z., LAZARIDES, E. and McINTOSH, J. R. (1977) A comparison of the distribution of actin and tubulin in the mammalian mitotic spindle as seen by indirect immunofluorescence, *J. Cell Biol.,* **72,** 552–67.
FUJIWARA, K. and POLLARD, T. D. (1976) Fluorescent antibody localization of myosin in the cytoplasm, cleavage furrow and mitotic spindle of human cells, *J. Cell. Biol.,* 848–75.
FUSELER, J. W. (1975) Temperature dependence of anaphase chromosome velocity and microtubule depolymerisation, *J. Cell Biol.,* **67,** 789–800.
INOUÉ, S. and RITTER, H. (1975) Dynamics of mitotic spindle organisation and

function, in *Molecules and Cell Movement,* pp. 3–30, eds S. Inoué and R. E. Stephens. Raven Press, N.Y.

LUYKX, P. (1970) Cellular mechanisms of chromosome distribution, *Int. Rev. Cytol.,* Supplement 2.

MABUCHI, I. and OKHUNO, M. (1977a) The effect of myosin antibody on the division of starfish blastomeres, *J. Cell Biol.,* **74,** 251–63.

McDONALD, K., PICKETT-HEAPS, J. D., McINTOSH, J. R. and TIPPIT, D. H. (1977b) On the mechanism of anaphase spindle elongation in *Diatoma vulgare, J. Cell Biol.,* **74,** 377–88.

McINTOSH, J. R., CANDE, W. Z. and SNYDER, J. A. (1975a) Structure and physiology of the mammalian mitotic spindle, in *Molecules and Cell Movement,* pp. 31–76, eds S. Inoué and R. E. Stephens. Raven Press, N.Y.

McINTOSH, J. R., CANDE, W. Z., SNYDER, J. and VANDERSLICE, K. (1975b) Studies on the mechanism of mitosis, *Ann. N.Y. Acad. Sci.,* **253,** 407–27.

McINTOSH, J. R., HEPLER, P. K. and VAN WIE, D. G. (1969) Model for Mitosis, *Nature,* **224,** 659–63.

McINTOSH, J. R. and LANDIS, S. C. (1971) The distribution of spindle microtubules during mitosis in cultured human cells, *J. Cell Biol.,* **49,** 468–97.

PERRY, M. M., JOHN, H. A. and THOMAS, N. S. T. (1971) Actin-like filaments in the cleavage furrow of the newt egg, *Exp. Cell Res.,* **65,** 249–53.

SALMON, E. D. (1975) Pressure-induced depolymerization of spindle microtubules. I. Changes in birefringence and spindle length, *J. Cell Biol.,* **65,** 603.

SCHLOSS, J. A., MILSTED, A. and GOLDMAN, R. D. (1977) Myosin subfragment binding for the localization of actin-like microfilaments in cultured cells, *J. Cell Biol.,* **74,** 794–815.

SCHROEDER, T. E. (1973) Actin in dividing cells: contractile ring filaments bind heavy meromyosin, *Proc. Natl. Acad. Sci.,* **70,** 1688–92.

SCHROEDER, T. E. (1975) Dynamics of the contractile ring, in *Molecules and Cell Movement,* eds S. Inoué and R. E. Stephens. Raven Press, N.Y.

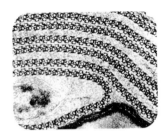

Chapter 7

Other motile systems in Protozoa

Protozoa comprise a large and very diverse phylum which, in addition to the amoeboid and axopodial movements of the sarcodines and the flagellar and axostylar movements of ciliates and flagellates, exhibits other fascinating examples of motility. As will become apparent, some movements based on microtubules and microfilaments resemble examples already discussed, but others appear to present novel mechanisms unknown elsewhere.

7.1 Contractile movements of ciliates

Several species of heterotrich and peritrich ciliates are capable of quite violent contraction. The heterotrichs, *Stentor* and *Spirostomum* particularly, have received a great deal of attention, as have the peritrichs *Vorticella* and *Carchesium*.

7.1.1 Myonemes and km fibres of heterotrichs
When subjected to chemical, mechanical or electrical stimuli, *Spirostomum* shortens to less than half its length, relaxes and then resumes swimming, often in the opposite direction. *Stentor* shows similar contraction, but only in the posterior end of the cell body (Fig. 7.1), and in addition is capable of considerable extension. The speed of contraction of these large ciliates is quite remarkable and has been estimated by cinematography at faster than 20 cm s^{-1}.

The basis for the contractile movements has fascinated scientists since before the turn of the century. By using electron microscopy,

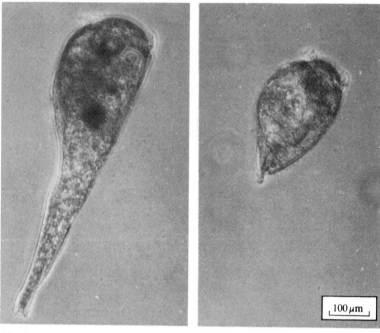

Fig. 7.1 Light micrographs showing *Stentor* in the partially extended and contracted states.

Randall and Jackson (1958) discovered two fibre systems in the cortical region of *Stentor* which they named M fibres, or myonemes, and km fibres (Fig. 7.2*a*). It is clear now that the myonemes are composed of microfilaments and the km fibres of microtubules, and comparable systems of these two organelles have been shown to exist in *Spirostomum* and other heterotrichs.

Both fibre systems change in length during the contractile process and their ultrastructure in the extended and the contracted states has been the subject of examination (Huang and Pitelka, 1973). Each myoneme in *Stentor* consists of a longitudinal bundle of 75–100, 4 nm

Fig. 7.2 Contraction of *Stentor*. (*a*) Electron micrograph of a transverse section through the cortex of *Stentor* fixed in the partially extended state, showing km fibres (km) and the myonemes (M) beneath them. (*b*)–(*c*) Electron micrographs of longitudinal sections of km fibres in the contracted (*b*) and fully extended (*c*) states. The width of the km fibres can be clearly correlated with the extent to which the component microtubule ribbons overlap. ((*a*) From B. Huang and D. Mazia, in *Molecules and Cell Movement*, p. 389, Raven Press, N.Y. (1975); (*b*) and (*c*) are from B. Huang and D. R. Pitelka (1973).)

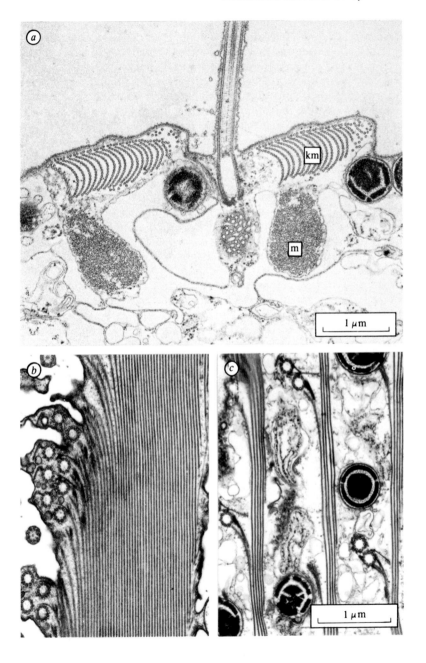

filaments arranged parallel to the long axis of the cell body, and immediately below a microtubular km fibre. By contrast, however, in the contracted state the myonemes appear composed of a dense aggregation of randomly oriented tubular filaments of 10–12 nm diameter. Such findings suggested to Huang and Pitelka that the shortening of the myonemes does not result from a simple sliding together of existing filaments, but from some change in the macromolecular conformation of the contractile elements of the myonemes.

We have mentioned that contractile heterotrichs also possess km fibres, and in *Stentor* these are composed of overlapping curved ribbons of microtubules. Each microtubule ribbon consists of 21 cross-linked microtubules which overlie each other and are attached at their anterior ends to a basal body complex. In the contracted state, as many as 40 microtubule ribbons overlap with their basal body origins closely opposed, whereas in the extended state the ribbons slide apart so that only 5 or 6 overlap, and the basal body origins to which they are anchored are well separated (compare Fig. 7.2*b* and *c*).

Bridges exist between adjacent microtubule ribbons within the km fibres, passing between the walls of the third and fourth microtubules of successive ribbons and in longitudinal sections these are seen to occur in pairs along the length of these microtubules with alternate spacings of 9 and 14 nm.

Contraction of the myonemes of *Stentor* has been found to be dependent upon the availability of calcium ions, since they remain extended in the presence of the divalent cation chelating agent EDTA, and their contractile state can be manipulated by the addition or removal of calcium ions. This has also been shown elegantly for *Spirostomum* by Ettienne (1970) who injected cells with aequorin and was able to correlate light emission, and hence calcium release, with contraction. Hence calcium ions appear to play the same role in the control of contractility as in striated muscle. A mechanism for altering the intracellular concentration of free calcium ions must exist, other than simply the control of flux across the plasma membrane, since normal contractions occur in calcium-free media, and there is no change in membrane potential during contraction.

One suggestion has been that since the myonemes are surrounded by enlarged cisternae of smooth endoplasmic reticulum, in which calcium has been shown to be present, changes in the levels of intracellular free calcium ions may be affected by release and uptake from these cisternae in a way comparable to the sarcoplasmic reticulum of muscle. Unlike muscle, however, the calcium activation is independent of the presence of ATP.

It is thought that the microtubule sliding within a km fibre may be a passive phenomenon during contraction, and the fact that inter-ribbon bridges detach during contraction is regarded as supporting this view. Re-extension, on the other hand, is much slower and apparently independent of the myonemes which elongate more rapidly than the overlying km fibres and consequently appear to buckle. During extension the inter-ribbon bridges of the km fibres are intact and are thought to be associated with active microtubule sliding.

Consequently, contraction and extension in *Stentor* seem to be under the control of two antagonistic systems. Essentially the same has been shown to be true for *Spirostomum* (Ettienne and Selitsky, 1974) where shortening can be inhibited reversibly with cytochalasin B, while extension appears to be dependent on the integrity of the cortical microtubules and the availability of metabolic energy.

7.1.2 Spasmonemes of peritrich ciliates

In peritrichs, such as *Vorticella*, the cell body is attached to the substrate by a stalk (Fig. 7.3a—d), and in contrast to the heterotrichs, contraction occurs only in the stalk region, rather than the cell body itself. A single dense filamentous fibre, known as a *spasmoneme*, runs the length of the stalk and is usually positioned asymmetrically within an elastic sheath and surrounded by stiffening fibres or bâtonnets (Fig. 7.3e). The latter are arranged helically in such a way that on contraction the whole stalk becomes helically twisted.

In several respects the spasmonemal contraction of peritrichs resembles the contraction of heterotrichs. In each case the rate of contraction is extremely rapid. Control appears related solely to the availability of calcium ions, and both differ from muscle contractile systems where calcium functions indirectly by regulating the rate at which ATP is hydrolysed.

Contraction of the *Vorticella* spasmoneme takes in the region of 4 ms – a rate much faster than that of striated muscle – whereas extension is slower and may take several seconds. Nevertheless, the forces developed by peritrich stalks have been measured as similar to those developed by muscles of metazoan cells. Contraction in glycerinated *Vorticella* can be induced by divalent cations in the absence of ATP hydrolysis, is reversed by treatment with EDTA, and single preparations can be taken through many cycles of contraction and extension in this way.

It has been suggested that contraction could result directly from the binding of calcium to the spasmoneme and Routledge *et al.* (1975) was able to measure this with an electron microprobe. Using the species *Zoothamnium geniculatum*, which has a spasmoneme large enough (1 mm $\times$ 30 μm) to be dissected by hand they discovered that contracted spasmonemes contained 3.81 g of Ca/kg of dry mass as opposed to 2.12 g/kg in extended ones.

The fine structure of the spasmonemes was similar in all the species

181

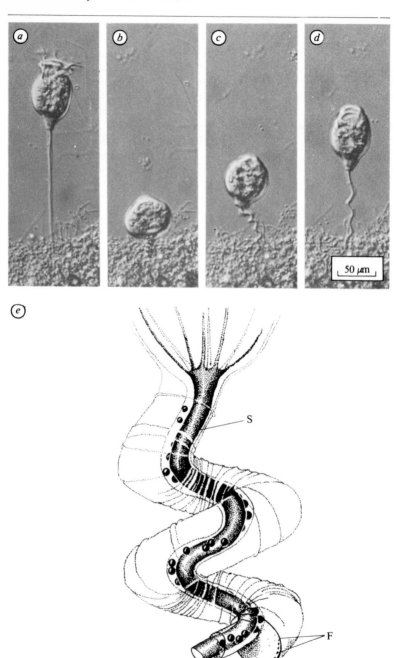

Fig. 7.3 Contraction of *Vorticella*. (*a*)–(*d*) Nomarski interference contrast micrographs of *Vorticella* showing their rapid contraction and gradual re-extension. (*e*) Diagram showing the spasmoneme (S) within the helically coiled stalk of a vorticellid. The stiffening fibres (F) can also be seen and run immediately beneath the sheath of the stalk. ((*e*) From W. B. Amos, in *Molecules and Cell Movement*, p. 411, Raven Press, N.Y. (1975).)

studied (Amos, 1972). In their contracted state spasmonemes were seen to be composed of a dense mass of longitudinally arranged 2–3 nm diameter filaments, which in some species were interspersed with mitochondria. In negatively stained preparations the filaments appeared beaded with a periodicity of approximately 3.5 nm. It is interesting to note that the spasmoneme also contains a system of membranous sacs which can accumulate calcium.

Analysis by SDS–polyacrylamide gel electrophoresis of whole spasmonemes has revealed a major protein band of molecular weight 20,000 which represented 60% of the stainable material, with most of the remaining proteins having molecular weights above 100,000. The absence of either actin or tubulin indicates a distinct difference from other motile systems. Likewise, their physical properties, as revealed by force-extension measurements which show that spasmonemes behave as a slightly vulcanised rubber (Weis-Fogh and Amos, 1972), serve to further illustrate this variance.

7.2 Movements of sporozoans

7.2.1 Pendulous movements of archigregarines

Sporozoan archigregarines of the genus *Selenidium* are parasites commonly found in the gut of polychaete worms and a few other marine invertebrates. The trophozoites of *Selenidium* are large elongated worm-like cells (100–400 μm × 10–25 μm). Each possesses a 'sucker' at one end, which anchors it to the gut wall, while the trophozoite performs rhythmic pendulous movements within the gut lumen (7.4*a*).

Since the early 1900s there has been speculation as to how these bending movements are brought about, and on the basis of light microscopy 'myocetes', made up of a network of circular, longitudinal and diagonally arranged fibrils, and myoneme fibrils, were regarded as the elements responsible. More recently, however, electron microscopy has gone some way towards clarifying the situation. The striated appearance of the trophozoites results from corrugation of the pellicle (Figs. 7.4*a*, *b*) which has been shown by scanning electron microscopy to vary during the beat cycles of the trophozoites. Beneath the folds of the pellicle, and running parallel to the long axis of the

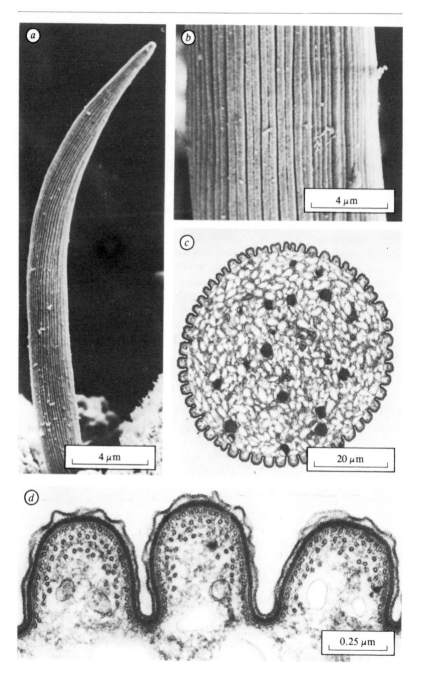

Fig. 7.4 *Selenidium.* (*a*), (*b*) Scanning electron micrographs of trophozoites of the archigregarine, *Selenidium fallax*, illustrating the characteristic folding of the pellicle in this organism. (*c*), (*d*) Transmission electron micrographs of transverse sections through a trophozoite showing clearly the pellicular folding and the rows of microtubules which are found beneath the folds. (Courtesy of J. S. Mellor.)

trophozoites, are at least two rows of microtubules (Fig. 7.4*d*) which ensheath the animals' cytoplasm. The microtubules are surrounded by electron-clear zones which separate them from their neighbours and microtubules in adjacent rows have centre to centre spacings of approximately 40 nm.

Since no other fibre system has been seen in *Selenidium,* much attention has focused on the role of the sub-pellicular microtubules, and experiments involving treatment with colchicine have certainly demonstrated their presence to be essential for the movements to take place (Stebbings *et al.*, 1974). Such experiments do not show, however, whether the microtubules function as motile or merely skeletal elements.

There is, however, indirect evidence which supports the view that the microtubules act as motile units, since Vivier and Henneré (1965) have found that they were absent in the intracellular immobile trophozoites of Coccidia, while Schrével (1971), on examining the trophozoites of a number of species of *Selenidium*, found that the number of microtubules beneath the pellicular folds was greater in those species which moved most actively.

Intriguingly, as well as being susceptible to colchicine, the movements of the trophozoites appear reversibly susceptible to cytochalasin B – a finding which indicates that one may have to look further than the microtubule arrays for an understanding of motility in this case.

7.2.2 Gliding movements of eugregarines
Eugregarines occur in the guts of many insects, where single individuals and also pairs in syzygy have the ability to glide through their surrounding medium without any apparent deformation in shape. This gliding movement has aroused particular interest because at the light microscope level there are no visible signs of motile organelles. Crawley (1902) questioned earlier suggestions that gliding in eugregarines was passive in nature and instead implicated a 'well-developed muscular system'. More recently, transmission and scanning electron microscope studies have helped to shed some light on the basis of this unique type of movement.

The cytoplasm in eugregarines is divided into an inner endoplasm containing numerous paraglycogen granules and an outer ectoplasm. The composition of the ectoplasmic layer is not well understood,

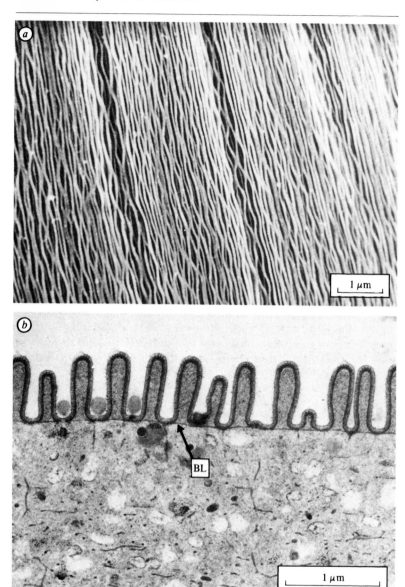

Fig. 7.5 Gliding movements of gregarines. (*a*) Scanning electron micrograph showing the pellicle of a eugregarine. The pellicle is both folded and apparently thrown into waves. (*b*) In contrast to archigregarines, the folds are separated from the main body of the organism by a basal lamina (BL) and lack microtubules. (Courtesy of Dr M. H. Walker.)

although various reports mention the presence of 'myonemes', 'tubular elements', 'an ectoplasmic network' and a 'fibrillar network', together with varying suggestions as to their function. Even so, it is difficult to pinpoint any ultrastructural component common to all eugregarines that glide.

As with the archigregarines, the pellicle in eugregarines is thrown into longitudinally orientated folds which run the length of the animal (Fig. 7.5a). They differ, however, in that the cytoplasm within the folds is not continuous with the main mass of the body, but is separated from it by a basal lamina (Fig. 7.5b).

Vivier (1968) describing deformations of the pellicular folds seen in sections suggested that the undulations of the folds could account for gliding, and scanning electron microscopy has shown that the folds in any gliding eugregarines are indeed thrown into waves, although the distribution of the waves may vary (Vavra and Small, 1969; Heller and Weise, 1973; Hildebrand and Vinckier, 1975; Walker *et al.*, 1979). There is now general agreement that the waves are not artefacts and the fact that animals which were seen to be non-motile before fixation showed no undulations has given support to the idea that the folds are involved in, and may be responsible for, the gliding movements.

The question remains as to how the undulations of the folds are generated. Although there is no conclusive evidence it is possible that they arise from within the folds themselves. Perhaps significantly, the presence of a row of longitudinally orientated electron-dense filaments (12–14 nm diameter), situated at the tip of each fold and closely associated with the innermost layer of the complex pellicle, has been reported in a variety of eugregarines. Also in *Gregarina garnhami* (Walker *et al.*, 1979), *G. hylobii* and *G. cuneata* (Rühl, 1976), a second system of less dense filaments has been identified between the outermost layers of the pellicle. It may be, therefore, that the waves are generated within the folds and that these filaments are directly involved in the process.

References

AMOS, W. B. (1972) Structure and coiling of the stalk in the peritrich ciliates *Vorticella* and *Carchesium*, *J. Cell Sci.*, **10**, 95–122.

CRAWLEY, H. (1902) Progressive movements in gregarines, *Proc. Acad. Nat. Sci., Philadelphia*, **54**, 4–20.

ETTIENNE, E. M. (1970) Control of contractility in *Spirostomum* by dissociated calcium ions, *J. Gen. Physiol.*, **56**, 168–79.

ETTIENNE, E. M. and SELITSKY, M. (1974) The antagonistic effects of antimitotic agents on contraction and re-extension in the ciliate *Spirostomum ambiguum*, *J. Cell Sci.*, **16**, 377–83.

HELLER, G. and WEISE, R. W. (1973) A scanning EM study of *Gregarina* sp. from *Udeopsylla nigra*, *J. Protozool.*, **20**, 61–4.

HILDEBRAND, H. F. and VINCKIER, D. (1975) Nouvelles observations sur la gregarine *Didymophes gigantea* Stein, *J. Protozool.,* **22,** 200–13.

HUANG, B. and PITELKA, D. R. (1973) The contractile process in the ciliate *Stentor coeruleus.* I. The role of microtubules and microfilaments, *J. Cell Biol.,* **57,** 704–28.

RANDALL, J. T. and JACKSON, S. (1958) Fine structure and function in *Stentor polymorphus, J. Biophys. Biochem. Cytol.,* **4,** 807–29.

ROUTLEDGE, L. M., AMOS, W. B., GUPTA, B. L., HALL, T. A. and WEIS-FOGH, T. (1975) Microprobe measurements of calcium-binding in the contractile spasmoneme of a vorticellid, *J. Cell Sci.,* **19,** 195–201.

RÜHL, H. (1976) Beitrag zur Physiologie der Bewegung der Gregarinen: Bewegungselements, Bewegungsweisen, *Z. Parasitenk.,* **48,** 199–214.

SCHRÉVEL, J. (1971) Contribution à l'étude des Selenidae parasites d'annelides polychètes II. Ultrastructure de quelque trophozoites, *Protistologica* **7,** 101–30.

STEBBINGS, H., BOE, G. S. and GARLICK, P. R. (1974) Microtubules and movement in the archigregarine, *Selenidium fallax, Cell Tiss. Res.,* **148,** 331–45.

VAVRA, J. and SMALL, E. B. (1969) Scanning E.M. of gregarines (Protozoa, Sporozoa) and its contribution to the theory of gregarine movement, *J. Protozool.,* **16,** 745–57.

VIVIER, E. (1968) L'organisation ultrastructurale corticale de la gregarine *Lecudina pellucida;* ses rapports avec l'alimentation et la locomotion, *J. Protozool.,* **15,** 230–46.

VIVIER, E. and HENNERÉ, E. (1965) Ultrastructures des stades végétatifs de la coccidie *Coelotropha durchoni, Protistologica* **1,** 89–104.

WALKER, M. H., MACKENZIE, C., BAINBRIDGE, S. P. and ORME, C. (1979) A study of the structure and gliding movement of *Gregarina garnhami* (Sporozoa, Protozoa). In preparation.

WEIS-FOGH, T. and AMOS, W. B. (1972) Evidence for a new mechanism of cell motility, *Nature,* **236,** 301–4.

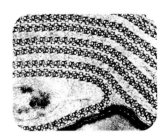

Index

Index